N°8 WIRE

Nº8 WIRE

The Best of Kiwi Ingenuity

Jon Bridges & David Downs

illustrations by Mathew Clark

Hodder Moa Beckett

'Necessity, who is the mother of invention...'

Plato
(427-347 BC), *The Republic*

'Where a new invention promises to be useful, it ought to be tried.'

Thomas Jefferson

DEDICATION

For Katherine. Thanks for all the toast. — *David*

For Rachael. Thanks. — *Jon*

ISBN 1-86958-820-7

© 2000 Text — Jon Bridges and David Downs
Reprinted 2001, 2003
The moral rights of the authors have been asserted.

© 2000 Illustrations — Mathew Clark

Published in 2000 by Hodder Moa Beckett Publishers Ltd
[a member of the Hodder Headline Group],
4 Whetu Place, Mairangi Bay, Auckland

Designed, typeset and produced by Hodder Moa Beckett Ltd
Film by Microdot, Auckland
Printed by Everbest Printing Co. Ltd., China

CONTENTS

ACKNOWLEDGEMENTS

This book was in gestation for quite a long time, and in that time we have been assisted by a great many people. We would like to thank the good people at Hodder Moa Beckett for their support and hard work; Rachael, Katherine and Jack for their quiet (mostly) sufferance of what turned out to be a marathon project; our friends and colleagues for their suggestions and advice; Tim Jackson, Damon Butler and the firm of Baldwin Shelston Waters for their advice on the patent process, and their assistance in patenting the 'Bath-b-Smaller'; the inventors and innovators, companies and individuals — too numerous to name here — who gave up time to talk to us and let us have an insight into their minds, and who hopefully won't mind our insights.

Special Acknowledgement

The authors and publisher wish to thank all the people and organisations who contributed photographs and provided information for this book. They have made every effort to trace the owners of copyright material, acknowledge sources and confirm facts contained in *No. 8 Wire*. Should any errors or omissions have occurred, they would like to offer their apologies. On receiving advice, acknowledgements will be made in further editions.

A special thank-you to Bob Riley and his book *Kiwi Ingenuity: A Book of New Zealand Ideas and Inventions* and to the wonderful people at NZEDGE.COM for their help and support.

Illustration Credits

The list below identifies the source of the photographs and illustrations (other than those drawn by Mathew Clark) included in this book. Any photographs that are not specifically identified are from the collections of the authors and publisher.

Abbreviations: t = top, b = bottom

p.9 New Zealand Wool Board; pp.11(t) & 12 Colin Murdoch; p.11(b) Paxarms; p.14 Lesley Hunter, courtesy of Warnham & Woburn Deer Society; pp.16 & 17(t) Allflex ear tags; p.17 Philip Holden; pp.20(t) & 21 Gallagher Group; p.20(b) Murray Ball; p.23 Cyclone; p.25 *New Zealand Herald*; p.27 Norma McCulloch; p.28 Pic Pac International; p.31 Tullen Industries; pp.32 & 33 Harco Sales; pp.34 & 35 Eric Adank; p.36 Novel Ways; p.38 Fisher & Paykel; p.42 Robinson Seismic; p.43 The Nobel Foundation; pp.45 & 47 Industrial Research Ltd; p.48 NDA Engineering; p.52 New Zealand Dairy Group; p.53 Ryan Manufacturing; pp.55 & 56 Brian Conlon; pp. 57 & 58 DB Group; p.61 Peter Bush; pp.62 & 63 Tantrix Games; p.65 Orica NZ; p.69 Vega Industries; p.75 Alexander Turnbull Library (F-83739-1/2); pp.76 & 77 Geoffrey Rodliffe & Ampersand; pp.80 & 81(b) Peter Bush; p. 82 & 83 AJ Hackett; p.84 NASA; p.85 Neil Harrap; p.87 The Particle Physics and Astronomy Research Council; p.93 Industrial Research Ltd; pp.96 & 97 Paul Crowther; p.99(b left) Astronomical Society of the Pacific; p.99(b) NASA; p.104 Nancy Adams; p.107 Bob Riley; p.109 Continuous Cycle Development; p.111 Bob Riley; p.112 Steve Stewart; p.113 Bob Riley; p.117 & 118 CWF Hamilton & Co.; p.119 Myark; pp.121 & 122 Britten Motorcycle Co.; p.124 Holder Enterprises; pp.125, 126 & 127 T & M Roycroft; p.129 News Media Auckland (Auckland Star Collection); p.131 Alexander Turnbull Library (F-65890-1/2 Ernest Marsden Collection); p.133(t) Alexander Turnbull Library (C-23002); p.133(b) Marching New Zealand; p.134 (t right) Wanganui District Council; p.134(t) Destination Wanganui; p.135(t) Waiouru Army Museum; p.135(b) Whanganui Regional Museum; p.141 Sonic VisioN; p.142 Quality Performers; p.143 Merck, Sharp & Dohme; p.144 Unifoot; p.147 Rob Buchanan; p.151 Buzzy Bee Toys Ltd; p.152 Glaxo Wellcome.

INTRODUCTION

When first we told people we were writing a book on great New Zealand inventions, many of them couldn't see how we would fill a whole book, when the 'only New Zealand inventors are Hamilton, Britten and Pearse'. Well, time and research have proven them well wrong. As you'll see when you read through these chapters, not only is the sheer number of New Zealand inventions astonishing, so is the diversity. In this book we examine subjects as different as milking machines and breast protectors, as fascinating as cryogenics and galaxies, and as predictable as Pavlova and suffrage.

The problem was not the lack of content; indeed, we had an embarrassment of stuff. We quickly realised that we couldn't hope to produce a complete list of New Zealand inventions, instead we have tried to produce a good representative sample of the ingenuity and inventiveness of the Kiwi. We set out give everyone a chance to read about something and exclaim 'Wow — I didn't know we thought of that!'

And along the way we learnt a lot about the inventive process and about the kinds of people that have great ideas. It seems to us that there are three major stages in the life of an invention: the creative process, where the idea is born; the development phase, where the original prototype is improved to make it a viable commercial product; and the 'sales' phase, where the product is 'marketed' (in the 'advertisement' sense of the term), the invention sold and where the inventor tries to make a buck out of his or her idea.

Kiwis' revered ingenuity, the 'No. 8 wire mentality' is at once a curse and a blessing. We New Zealanders like to see ourselves as the underdog, creating something out of nothing when the need arises, and this can lead to some great innovations. But inventiveness and improvisation can also lead to the idea that 'good enough' is good enough, when in fact if an invention is to be commercially successful, it must be perfect. From our discussions with inventors, the actual process of creation, the act of coming up with a new idea, or a new slant on an existing idea, is what they love about inventing. The creative 'spark' is what fires them, but following up on that idea, turning that spark into a flame, is where 90 percent of inventors fall down.

The unfortunate reality of the modern world is that without a 'market-driven' focus, many inventions will stagnate or die. It routinely takes years and years to get from the beginning of an idea to the product in the marketplace. The person who is still there at the end of those years makes the money and takes the glory. Invention is only part of invention.

And is enough being done to support these creative people in their endeavours? Probably not. Many of the organisations and individuals we talked to are struggling financially, and receive little or no assistance from anyone. While our popular conception of ourselves as a nation of innovators might be justified, the New Zealand environment certainly doesn't beget a financially successful invention. Other countries have government schemes to help foster the development of new ideas, but with a few exceptions, ours doesn't. The impressive list of inventions gathered in this book alone should convince anyone that we have genuine ideas that deserve to be taken seriously, developed professionally and supported financially.

If you've got comments, suggestions, additions or thoughts on the contents of the book, or for a lead on some more information, feel free to contact the authors at **inventors@eureka.co.nz**. But for now read on, and hopefully you'll be as surprised and inspired as we were.

1. ALL CREATURES GREAT AND SMALL

Sheep, ear tags and the tranquilliser gun

New Zealand was and, to a large extent, still is an agrarian economy. In all our traditions and popular lore, the country was built on the back of good, honest, God-fearing farmers, quietly tilling the earth and tending the flocks, and in the process ensuring our country's place as the 'farmyard of England'.

It's only natural, then, that New Zealand inventions and innovations have a 'farming' air about them. Not (just) an odour of silage, more the impression that these inventions were born of mother necessity, and sired by father practicality. Not the frivolous 'invention of the cellphone', nor the idle 'creation of the frisbee' for us. No, on the whole, New Zealand inventions are bound to be far more practical and applicable to life on the farm.

Perendale, Drysdale and Corriedale

Half sheep, half...another type of sheep

New Zealanders didn't invent sheep, although we would have if it weren't for the small stumbling block of them having already been invented. However, sheep were brought to New Zealand early and eventually thrived (although the first sheep were two luckless Merino brought here by Cook in 1773, and dead by 1774). Sheep form half the backbone of the New Zealand economy, the heart of our farming culture and the leg of our Sunday roasts. Say 'New Zealand' to a foreigner and chances are they'll say either 'We kicked your arse in the World Cup' or 'Sheep'. New Zealand is the second largest producer and exporter of wool in the world (at 203,000 tonnes in 1997/98). In this endeavour we are beaten only by Australia, and far outstrip our nearest rival — China (who also buy a lot of our wool).

Surprisingly the size of the New Zealand flock has been in steady decline — from 69 million in 1984 to around 47 million in 1998. Which begs the question: where have they all gone? We're talking about the disappearance of 22 million sheep — 88 million leg roasts, or 25.1 roasts for every man, woman and child among us. Surely we would have noticed the shortage in mint sauce by now? Forget 'Who ate all the pies?', how about 'Who ate all the sheep?'?

But, of course, despite the ready-made varieties of sheep available to us, and in the true spirit of Kiwi ingenuity, we decided to invent our own flavours to suit our own geography. The Merino is the most popular breed of sheep in the world, but it proved too sissy for our climate, so we began to experiment. The New Zealand Romney is a distinct breed developed from the English Romney to form the basis of our meat and wool industry, and almost 60 percent of our flock.

Geoffrey Sylvester Peren of Massey University was a sheep researcher at what was, in the 1950s, a solely agricultural college. He invented a crossbreed of Cheviot and Romney to meet the needs of hill country farmers on developing land. The Perendale is a hardy, low maintenance kind of all-terrain sheep for either wool or meat production. Mr Peren's genetic innovation was a resounding success. At one stage there were over 10 million Perendale sheep in New Zealand and in 1975 the breed was officially recognised by Australia (who presumably said, 'Hey, aren't you Perendale?').

The Drysdale sheep was originated by Professor FW Dry who discovered the sheep gene that affected the hairiness of the fleece in Romney sheep. Formerly these sheep were culled as being too 'hairy' — not fine enough. Professor Dry teamed up with an English company who wanted the wool from these extra hairy sheep for carpets, and developed the breed. Because he was breeding sheep that might taint the national Romney flock, Dry's programme was rigorously curtailed by the government of the time until the demand for the flock grew. Now New Zealand and Australia both have considerable Drysdale flocks.

But New Zealand's most successful sheep invention is undoubtedly the Corriedale. This is a large-framed, hornless sheep, with dark pigmented skin on nostrils and lips and a heavy fleece of long-stapled, bulky wool (you know the one). The Corriedale was developed in New Zealand and Australia during the late 1800s by crossing Lincoln or Leicester rams with Merino females. The breed is now distributed worldwide, making up the greatest population of all sheep in South America, and thrives throughout Asia, North America and South Africa. While its popularity suggests it is the second most significant breed in the world after Merinos, it now makes up only about 5 percent of our national flock.

Of course, the real joy of the sheep

Corriedale

Drysdale

Perendale

invention industry is having the sheep named after you. Peren and Dry (and presumably some unknown Mr or Ms Corrie) are now forever immortalised in wool. As New Zealanders we are more likely than any other nationality to one day have a sheep named after us. To try it on and see how it fits, simply add the word 'dale' to the end of your name. How does it sound? Good, I bet.

Woolrest Sleeper

Yes madam, genuine sheepskin

All was not well at Hallmark Industries. Although the company was selling upwards of 45,000 backpacks a year, the writing was on the wall. High labour costs in New Zealand suggested to them that a business importing raw materials, then exporting manufactured goods that were more expensive than those available overseas, was swimming against the tide. The Hallmark team, led by Bill Hall, Gordon Chesterton and Bruce Weeks, set out to find something else they could make. Something from indigenous New Zealand materials.

What more indigenous material than wool? Word reached them of an Australian company making traditional Greek 'flokati' rugs commercially. If they could copy the rugs, and

the government imposed an import tariff on them, they would have a good local market for a lovely rug product. Knowing nothing about rugs, they offered to buy the manufacturing technique off the Australian crowd, who quoted them $100,000 — the cheeky buggers. Luckily, somebody at the New Zealand Wool Board said, 'That technique is in a book I've got.' Flokati rugs are white, with a shaggy, matted look that is traditionally gained by leaving the woven rug under a waterfall. The Hallmark team bought a whole lot of weaving machines and perfected the designs for vats through which water was pumped to create an artificial waterfall effect.

The rugs were perfect, but the government would not put a tariff on the imported versions. Despite being made of New Zealand wool, the Australian versions were cheaper! Things looked grim. Then luck stepped in, and along with brilliant marketing turned a copycat product that was going nowhere into a brand new, worldwide household commodity. A customer asked if he could have a rug made to fit his bed, as he had bad arthritis and was hoping the rug might help. When he returned weeks later raving about the improvement in his condition, wheels began to turn. Bill Hall had the foresight to immediately commission a huge study at the University of Waikato. The results were overwhelmingly positive for his invention, and the Woolrest Sleeper was born.

Sales were mail order only at first, but they

boomed. Retailers soon demanded the product and before long Selwyn Toogood was promoting Woolrest Sleepers all over New Zealand, and the market for them was strong in the United Kingdom, Australia and the United States. Copycats sprung up (50 in the States alone), but Woolrest were hardly in a position to complain and had to compete on the basis of quality and the name Woolrest.

At the peak of production the factory was going six days a week, 24 hours a day, turning out 100 tonnes of wool a month — a huge quantity. By the time Bill Hall and his Hallmark team sold the venture Woolrest had become a household name, and not just in New Zealand.

The genius of Bill Hall and his team was to take an old product (the 'Golden Fleece' of ancient legend is said to have been a flokati rug) and re-introduce it to the world. And Hallmark? Having a new product to replace the outdoor goods business, Bill Hall and his shareholders sold that to Great Outdoors.

The tranquilliser gun

If you love something, shoot it full of tranquilliser

Colin Murdoch with a tranquil-looking lioness, thanks to animal friendly syringe fire.

If you were alive during the 1970s, you would have enjoyed the TV show 'Daktari'. Basically an action/drama series about a vet on the

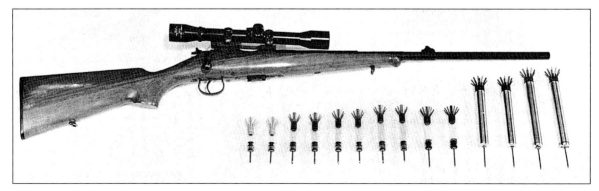

savannahs of Africa, pulling thorns from lions' paws and shooting zebras with a tranquilliser gun. How pleasing, then, to learn that Daktari wouldn't have been half the swashbuckling man-about-the-savannah that he was without the help of a New Zealander.

Say you're a vet, a ranger, a zoologist or animal physiologist keen to study animals without killing them. Before the invention of the tranquilliser gun and darts, the only way to catch a live animal without killing it was to chase it down in a vehicle, and lasso it with a pole and a loop of rope and wrestle it to the ground where it could be safely injected. Obviously if the animal was a slow one, the vehicle may not have been needed. If it was a dangerous one then even this method would have been too risky, and the animal would need to be trapped. It wasn't until 1959 that the tranquilliser gun was invented and perfected — and it took a New Zealander to manage it.

Looking down the barrel

Colin Murdoch's tranquilliser guns are modified pistols or rifles, with interchangeable barrels for different calibre syringe projectiles. The power is provided by ordinary sport-shooting cartridges. Each gun has a twisting dial that can be set to any of 32 positions. The dial controls a valve forward of the pre-expansion chamber and between the cartridge and the projectile.

The more the valve is opened, the further the projectile will fly. With the valve at minimum you can shoot an animal in a cage a few feet away, at maximum it will fire 150 m. Using a special scope that Colin also invented (and which was snaffled by Nato in 1974 for their troops) the range of the animal can be determined and the angle of elevation of firing can be adjusted to control the velocity at which the syringe hits the animal: fast for thick hides, slow for thin hides.

The syringes themselves are incredibly strong and light polycarbonate plastic with a needle threaded onto the front, and a small shuttlecock-like tail on the back to give very accurate shooting. On impact a special needle and valve system lets a free piston inside the syringe push the dose into the animal. It's all brilliant.

Let's have a quick look at the difficulties the task poses. First, you have to deliver a dose of tranquilliser into the body of the animal, so you need a syringe that doubles as a projectile and delivers the dose upon impact. Next, you don't want to hurt the animal with the impact, so you have to be able to control the velocity of the flying drugs so that, no matter how far away you are from the animal, the needle just sticks into the skin without breaking a bone. The guns to shoot these syringes will have to have variable power, and variable calibre to accommodate different dose syringes. This invention was waiting for an expert in gun making, animal physiology, ballistics, pharmaceuticals and anaesthesia.

Colin Murdoch of Timaru was working with colleagues studying introduced Himalayan thar (wild goat-antelope!) populations in New Zealand, and had the idea that if a dose of tranquilliser could be safely projected into one of the animals it would be a lot easier to catch, examine, tag and release them. Murdoch was a pharmacist who had a veterinary practice on the side. During the Second World War, rifles and shotguns were not imported into New Zealand, so, as a serious hunter, Colin became an expert at fixing and modifying guns. With the motive and the means, Murdoch began to develop the range of tranquilliser rifles, pistols and darts that revolutionised the way animals were studied and treated all over the world.

At first Colin tested the system on dog-tucker rams in Timaru, then he travelled the world looking for unsuspecting animals to test his invention on. From long range he anaesthetised hundreds and hundreds of kangaroos, zebra, crocodiles and other animals. From the moment he produced the first gun in New Zealand, it became known. He patented it and started getting inquiries from overseas. Colin's company, Paxarms (pax=peace + arms) began exporting the systems from Timaru to over 150 countries. Every time they sent one to an area, other zoologists got to hear about it and demand would grow. Both Colin and his invention played large parts in the domestication of deer

(see next story), Colin himself riding in the helicopter with Sir Tim Wallis when they tranquillised and caught the first three deer for Wallis' experiments in 1964.

Colin has 17 patents for the products and has won design and inventors' awards both in New Zealand and overseas. And the tranquilliser gun is not even the most influential of Murdoch's inventions. He invented pre-filled, sterile, disposable plastic syringes for humans and multi-dose automatic vaccinator syringe hypodermic guns for animals, and these are used today in the billions around the world each year.

So, hey, next time you're crouched over a heavily sedated cheetah, administering much needed dental work and then watching it awake none the worse and wander off majestically into a safari sunset, please think of Colin Murdoch, the Timaru Daktari who made it all possible.

Deer farming

Tall fences and lots of Bambi quips make for a lucrative new industry

Humans have been hunting deer for thousands of years, but in New Zealand the period has been considerably shorter. Deer were

Stags at bay.

introduced for game hunting purposes initially, but quickly became a pest — eating more than their share of native vegetation — and the government hired 'cullers' for a period to reduce the numbers. Most amateur hunting had been for the hunter's table, until in the early 1970s when venison began to be processed and exported in large quantities, and hunters could get good money for something that was just wandering around in the bush. But this required much wandering around in the bush, getting lost, getting hypothermia, or hanging out of helicopters with a rifle. Better to put all the deer in one place and look after them. Deer farming was invented.

The most efficient way to get meat to eat is to domesticate, breed and then kill some sort of animal species. Throughout history, various animals have been tested for domestication in a global process of trial and error. Some 10,000 years ago sheep, goats and pigs were domesticated, then cows 8000 years ago. Next were horses, donkeys and water buffalo. And by about 5000 years ago, the llama, camel, yak and reindeer were also tamed (along with banteng and the gaur, but I've never heard of those). For 5000 years after that, no further (large) mammals were domesticated. None at all. And it wasn't for a lack of trying.

Unlike sheep, cattle and other animals, deer do not always get along with each other. They herd during part of the year, but during mating season they are very territorial. They

also display behaviour which makes it inconvenient to keep them in one place. While not an inherently nasty animal (which is what has kept the zebra safe from domestication) they show a tendency (like antelopes and gazelles) to panic and scatter when frightened. Discovering the way around these difficulties was what made the practice possible, and not only possible, but practical, efficient and worthwhile.

In 1973 Dr Ken Drew borrowed a few deer and set up an experimental farm, along with MAF vet Les Porter. The two set out to put a

Venison Fillets in Mushroom & Wine Sauce

Ingredients (serves 4-6)

1 T lemon juice
500 g venison fillet steak, cut into 6 slices
1/4 c flour, seasoned with salt and pepper
100 g butter
4 rashers bacon, chopped
2 spring onions, finely chopped
1 c red wine
3 c sliced mushrooms
1 c cream
1 T chopped fresh parsley to garnish

Method

Sprinkle lemon juice over fillets, then coat with seasoned flour. Melt butter in large frying pan or casserole dish and sauté bacon and spring onions, stirring constantly, for 2½-3 minutes, until spring onions are tender but not browned. Add fillets and sauté for 4-5 minutes, until browned. Reduce heat to low, pour in wine and simmer gently for 10 minutes. Transfer meat to ovenproof serving dish. Add mushrooms and cream to pan, and cook over low heat for 3 minutes, stirring constantly. Pour sauce over steaks and cook covered at 180°C for 20 minutes. Sprinkle with parsley and serve immediately.

Copyright © Philip Holden 1995
Holden, Philip, *Holden's New Zealand Venison Cookbook*, Hodder Moa Beckett, Auckland, 1995, p.49.

structure around deer farming, to formulate the basic management practices. They were generally considered 'crackpots', but they persevered, and had a large part in establishing New Zealand's world-leading industry. There are 1.8 million farmed deer in New Zealand, of which only 600,000 are (very tired looking) males.

Our practice has spread to other parts of the world, but today New Zealand still has the largest and most advanced deer farming industry in the world — approximately 85 percent of all venison served in restaurants in the United States comes from New Zealand. So successful was New Zealand venison that an 'appellation', or a kind of quality-controlled brand name, has been created. Now we don't eat 'venison', we eat 'Cervena'. Whatever the marketing department want to call it, $200 million a year in exports (plus about $50 million worth of velvet) is still a lot of Bambi steaks.

Allflex ear tags

Keeping tabs on your stock

Sometimes inventions aren't cool or glamorous. Sometimes they don't seem very ground-breaking and they aren't exciting to teenagers — even if they involve body piercing. Unfortunately, the way with inventions is that the ones that are the least fun to look at are often the most fun to make money from. No matter what the salespeople at Allflex will tell you, the Allflex stock tags are one of those inventions.

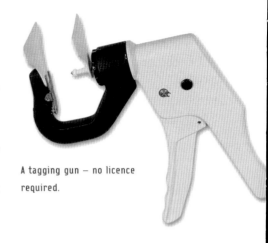

A tagging gun — no licence required.

Put simply, the Allflex tag system is a farm-management tool. It is not an invention that can be described as a first, but it deserves its place in this book by being an innovation that made their product easily the best. Before the Allflex system was developed, stock were identified by either a metal tag or a one-piece plastic tag. These tags weren't easy to see, they rusted, they fell off. The Allflex system solved those problems and enabled farmers to improve the efficiency of their work.

You might be wondering how a tag helps farmers. Well, I warned you the answer was not going to be astonishing, but I'll try and make it as exciting as possible. Imagine you are being chased full-tilt through a field by a bull. The bull is running you down, its hooves heavy on the ground, its red eyes crazed. You rush headlong towards the fence, but can you possibly reach it before the bull gores you?

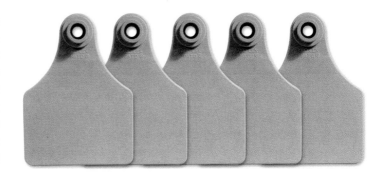

Looking over your shoulder you see by the two-piece flexible polyurethane tags through its left ear that it is a male. You knew that already. The front tag is blue, so it was born in 1998, if you could see that back tag you would know by the colour that it was one of your own bulls. The bull lowers its heaving head and you feel its hot breath. As your life flashes in front of your eyes, you read the coded numbers and letters on the patented Allflex Laza-tag and the bull's life story flashes before your eyes as well — you know about its parents, that it was a twin, what percentage of pure-bred it is. Just before you are raised on the bull's razor-sharp horns, you give a little laugh. There is no notch on the tag — the bull's semen was under-performing and he was due to be culled, but now he's culling you. 'Ah, those ironic bulls' is your last thought.

How much more exciting could an invention be? In 1964 a Taranaki farmer called Brian Murphy conceived the idea of a new system of cattle identification. The Duotag and its applicator were the result. The company that made them and the company that sold them eventually merged to become Allflex. The product was immediately better than anything else on the market, but in 1971 the use of the male tag, in combination with the applicator to pierce the ear and apply the tag in one operation, made the system unique and patentable. It was patented worldwide, and successful exporting commenced. Such a simple system is bound to have imitators, and throughout the 1970s, Allflex took legal action in the United States against patent infringements. Finally in 1982 they won those battles and were awarded punitive damages.

Allflex products are now manufactured in four countries, and marketed in all major countries, making Allflex the world's most widely used animal identification tag. Orders of 10 million plus tags are not uncommon and the tags have been used not only on sheep and cattle but on fur seals, bears, fish, penguins and even lampposts. Allflex are the self-professed 'number one livestock identification company in the world', and why not when they make something as romantic-sounding as a system for the 'revolutionary electronic tracking of animals from birth to slaughter'.

Allflex tags are available in many fashion colours.

Ear tag super-model.

2. GOOD FENCES MAKE GOOD NEIGHBOURS

Electric fences, slugs and snails, and the fake symbol of Kiwi ingenuity

New Zealand is a land of neighbours. Both near and far neighbours and the kind that actually neigh (or baa or moo). Early in our European history we had to deal with the problem of keeping stock where it was supposed to be. A country was being domesticated and the geography demanded a hell of a lot of fencing. It was almost a hundred years before New Zealanders really changed the methods of fencing we imported with our first stock. Some of those imported fencing methods led to disaster — the rampant weed, gorse, was originally introduced as a hedgerow and is now the yellow-flowered scourge of many hillsides.

The wire and batten fence, in various incarnations, served to satisfy our fencing needs for the first century or so of settlement. Fences need gates, so there was the ubiquitous 'Taranaki gate', a concoction of wire and wood that appears, in our investigations, to have no confirmed lineage, and indeed seems to be an idea that has grown up simultaneously at many places around the world, and been variously dubbed 'the Australian gate', 'the Waikato gate', even 'the Channel Islands gate'.

The traditional fences and gates were sufficient to do the job, so why the change? For Kiwis, it seems, necessity is the mother of invention, but certainly possibility is the curious father, fossicking around in the middle of the night where he probably shouldn't be.

Now, invention doesn't need three parents so maybe we should just say that, as far as New Zealand invention goes, No. 8 wire must be the milkman of invention.

No. 8 wire

*Our imported symbol
of invention*

No. 8 wire is legendary as the stuff of all New Zealand inventions. The phrase 'No. 8 wire' is inextricably entangled with many of our icons of Kiwiness, including Barry Crump, Fred Dagg, self-sufficiency and 'she'll be right'. It is ironic, weird, and a little bit disappointing, then, that No. 8 wire is itself an import.

No. 8 wire is actually more properly called 'ISWG#8' — a clumsy acronym that stands for the British 'Industry Standard Wire Gauge 8'. Apparently different kinds of wire are measured and named by their thickness or diameter, with the thickest called zero gauge, an impressive half an inch, or 10 mm, thick. This is not so much wire as a rod. It seems seven (5 mm) and eight (4 mm) gauge are the easiest to handle, and therefore the most popular for fencing throughout the world.

It was in the 1860s that New Zealanders began importing wire for fencing. By the 1880s eight gauge wire was the most popular, as seven gauge was too thick. And so it was that No. 8 wire became ubiquitous in New Zealand; our country was, if not covered by it, at least divided up into tiny pieces by it, and every single inch of it was imported from England, Belgium, Germany or Australia.

It wasn't until 1963 that New Zealand Wire Industries (now Cyclone) began to make wire in New Zealand, putting an end to a century of wire importing. High-tensile wire soon replaced the old steel wire, and No. 8 gave way to the new 2.5 mm, which is lighter, cheaper and stronger.

Because No. 8 wire was available at all times around the farm, it was put to millions of uses: to tie, to bind, to construct, repair, modify and fashion things. It was often used to make the prototypes of real innovations, later manufactured properly. No. 8 wire came to stand for adaptability. In fact, at the annual agricultural Fieldays show near Hamilton, they have a competition for making new creations utilising good old No. 8. There are even rumours that Zinzan Brooke, the most famous No. 8 of recent times, was in fact fashioned out of wire.

As flexible and useful as No. 8 wire was, for things other than fencing, it was eventually found wanting in one important area — fence making. Perversely for the great icon of workbench utility, it was the need for something more flexible in the fencing world that led to a great New Zealand invention.

Gallagher and the electric fence

*Itchy horse's ass turns wire
into power – and money*

One of New Zealand's greatest contributions to the world of agriculture came with the combination of two quite different technologies — the fence and electricity.

Imagine a fence that did not rely on sheer strength for its effectiveness. This allows the fence to be light, and therefore easily portable. Now the way is open to develop a flexible fencing system that suits modern, specialised and precise farming techniques.

Even if you are from the city (or, maybe, especially if you are from the city) the electric fence is an integral part of New Zealand life. Everyone has experienced being on the cow's end of it, climbing over without touching it, saying 'Do you think it's on?', testing it with a blade of grass, trying to touch it between pulses, hearing the metronomic ticking as it interferes with the radio reception, or watching Wal in the *Footrot Flats* cartoon as he straddles the fence, his gummies sinking into the mud.

In the 1930s Bill Gallagher developed a plan to keep his horse Joe from scratching itself on the family car (an Essex, incidentally). Mr Gallagher cunningly connected the car to an electrical supply. When the horse rocked the car, pressing his itchy horsehide against the car in search of an appropriately scratchy sticky-out bit, a triggering device sent a current through the car, and through Joe. It worked. Animals will go to similar lengths as we will to avoid electric shocks. Bill Gallagher did not go on to patent his electric car protector (we can only speculate why not — perhaps because it was total overkill), but he did begin experimenting with electrified fences — and not just around cars but around paddocks.

The idea wasn't originally Bill's. 'I read in America where they were using electrified wire to hold stock.' But it wasn't the original idea that mattered in this case. It was that Bill developed the idea from that seed to a successful electric-fence product which was later to return to America, and elsewhere, as the best electric fence technology in the world.

To begin with, Bill Gallagher linked about a mile of fence on his Waikato farm to the mains power supply. It worked fine, but laws at the time prevented the mains power supply from being used in this way. So Mr Gallagher developed a battery-powered version and by 1940 he was selling them. 'The neighbours wanted these things, so I made them some; I'd make half a dozen and go out on the road, sell them, leave them

Archaeological study dates this original Gallagher Energizer to 1938.

WHEN WAL' COMES I DON'T THINK I'LL MENTION MY LITTLE SKIRMISH WITH THE GIANT HARE...

IT'S NOT THAT I'M ASHAMED OF BEING BEATEN... I FOUGHT A HARD, FAIR FIGHT!

I JUST DON'T THINK HE'D UNDERSTAND THE DIFFICULTY OF HAVING ON A HARE WITH A BLACK BELT IN JUDO...

... I THINK I'LL TELL HIM I'M DOIN' YOGA.

on a month's trial, and people would mostly pay for them.'

In 1961 New Zealand law was changed to allow electric fences to be connected to the mains electricity supply. At that time, Ruakura scientist Doug Phillips took this opportunity to begin experimenting in technology for mains-powered electric fences. At first he thought he should electrify the ground! Not surprisingly, that turned out to be unworkable, so he developed a low-impedance electric fence with a very high surge of power. Problems battery-powered fences had when vegetation caused shorting were solved, because the high power just burned any vegetation off the wires! Doug Phillips' new solution made feasible electric fences that encompassed whole farms, and the Gallagher team (along with other New Zealand fence manufacturers) were quick to recognise the brilliance of the idea and copy it.

With innovative New Zealand technology like the low-impedance fence, Gallagher launched a successful export campaign. To date, the Gallagher group have secured over 100 worldwide patents for their products and processes and still lead the world in electric-fence technology. Not only sheep and cattle, but antelope, kangaroos and zebra are contained by New Zealand electric fences around the world. Gallagher have also sold over 6000 km of electric fencing to Malaysia to keep elephants out — or is that to keep elephants in? Basically to keep elephants.

Not only has the electric fence proven to be a fine New Zealand export, it has also encouraged innovative farming in this country. During the 1960s and '70s, the electric fence began to change farming practice, especially in the dairy and beef industries, by allowing flexible and more efficient grazing. These new practices helped make New Zealanders the best and most efficient farmers in the world. And if you want to argue with that, you can argue with Bill Gallagher and his electrocuting car!

Bill and Mrs Gallagher made a zappy couple.

Slug fence

Humane protection for buttercups and super-toms

Just as the electric fence caused innovation in farming techniques, it also set off reverberations in other areas of the fencing market in New Zealand, particularly in the tricky invertebrate fence industry.

In 1992, after years of trial and error, Bob Tait of Auckland came up with a way to keep slugs and snails off his lettuces without killing them. A simple wire loop, laid around the perimeter of the lettuce area, attached to a nine-volt battery, served to repel the gastropods by giving them the kind of shock you get when you lick a nine-volt battery (except imagine your whole body is a tongue). The slugs and snails slink away disappointed, stunned and sore, still hungry, but not dead.

Let's look at it this way. Keeping slugs and snails off lettuces without killing them (and without employing a student to just sit there picking them off) is a perfectly good invention. What stops it being a great invention, a rich-and-famous-making, mana-bringing giant of simple thought and clever engineering?

Just one thing — that while quite a few people care if slugs and snails are on lettuces, very few people care whether the slugs and snails that are not on lettuces are alive. It's not the invention itself, but our attitude towards slugs and snails that holds this invention back. Bob is just waiting for a huge slug-and-snail attitude swing. It might not happen soon, but when the slug-and-snail rights movement gains a foothold, Bob Tait will live like a king!

Eze-Pull fencing tool

Where rhyming meets fencing

In New Zealand there are millions of kilometres of fences. On every kilometre of fence, there are hundreds of battens and posts. On every batten there are at least five staples. That means at least 500 million staples. If you take a piece of fence down and you want to save the wire or re-use the posts, you have to take all those staples out. Any farmer will tell you that taking thousands of staples out of a piece of fence is a hell of a task, a horrible job. It's a hard

enough job to have seen plenty of fence burnt or rolled up and buried, rather than bother.

In 1975, in a Whatawhata Hills farm shed in the Waikato, an old Post Office wire crimper was modified to make the first innovation in staple-pulling technology the world had seen in a century.

Chris Johnson had a kind of head start — he was the great-nephew of Ernest Rutherford. While Ernest Rutherford was an intensely theoretical inventor, working out how to take apart the tiniest particle known to humans, Chris was the archetypal New Zealand handyman and farmer, and he worked out how to take a fence apart. If this was a patriotic TV show about real New Zealanders and their pioneering inventions, the voice-over for this part would say, 'A fence is as hard to split as an atom and it took a Kiwi to do both!'

Chris was a farmer and a bagpipe player. He says, 'Every time I stripped a fence, my fingering ability became less, so I decided to improve the staple-puller.' Chris realised immediately that he had something that others would want.

The old staple-puller was neither a good puller nor a good wire cutter. The Eze-Pull is a good wire cutter and a good puller. It is so effective that you can get almost any staple: 'If you can see it, you can pretty much get it out.' On top of that, the Eze-Pull is much safer than its predecessor — it is very hard to pinch yourself with it. Chris reckons it has saved the country

The Eze-Pull in all its
staple-pulling glory.

hundreds of thousands of dollars in injuries.

The Eze-Pull has won every award that can be won in the national Fieldays award system, and Chris himself sometimes can't believe that it has all come together so well. His company has been marketing it internationally for over 10 years and sold tens of thousands of the tools all over the world. The main market is the United States and Canada, with most contractors in the States now using an Eze-Pull. They also sell to the British Isles, Ireland, France and Scandinavia.

The last word is Chris': 'There is a whole raft of inventors out there that you'll never hear of because they're doing it every day, because they have to innovate in their jobs as

engineers. I'm not particularly special because engineers do it all the time as part of their everyday job. Ernest Rutherford was a

physicist — I'm just a farmer who is handy with his hands. I see that as an art form.'

The Staplelok fencing system

Helping us all be Barry Crump

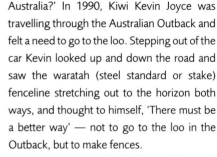

The story of the Staplelok fencing system starts with a topic that is often foremost in New Zealanders' minds: 'What is wrong with Australia?' In 1990, Kiwi Kevin Joyce was travelling through the Australian Outback and felt a need to go to the loo. Stepping out of the car Kevin looked up and down the road and saw the waratah (steel standard or stake) fenceline stretching out to the horizon both ways, and thought to himself, 'There must be a better way' — not to go to the loo in the Outback, but to make fences.

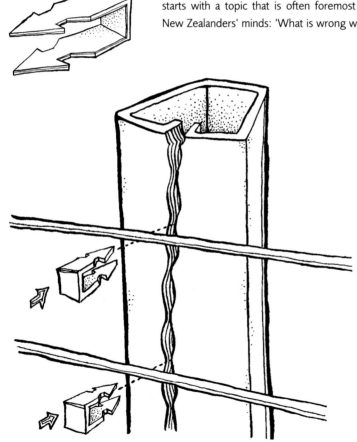

A steel waratah has holes in it through which the wire is passed. In a very long fence it is difficult to feed the wire through the holes and tension it, so the wires are just tied to the holes with another bit of wire. It's a pretty Mickey Mouse system. The advantage of waratahs over traditional wooden post and batten fences is that they are light and easy to transport, which is a huge factor when making fences many kilometres long in remote areas. Kevin came home and developed a system that had all of the advantages of the waratah, with none of the disadvantages. His first system worked, but in 1991 and 1992 he took the system to the technicians at the University of Auckland. Using computer-aided design and manufacturing machines they made the system 15 percent cheaper, 60 percent stronger and 15 percent lighter — at the same time making it work better!

Staplelok fenceposts are made from high-tensile, galvanised steel, with a scalloped groove down one side of the post. The staples that hold the wires to the fence are banged into the groove with an ordinary hammer and lock into place. They will not slide or come out until removed with the Staplelok staple remover. In fact it would take between 300 and 400 kg of force to pull the staple out without the staple remover. The posts are extremely strong and very light (2.2 kg) compared to fenceposts — a farmer can carry up to 20 at one time. Remember even Colin Meads could only be expected to carry one or two wooden fenceposts. Using a special hand-held and hand-powered rammer (instead of either digging holes or using a 550 kg hydraulic rammer mounted on a tractor) one person can easily put the posts into the ground. For a job like fencing, which is incredibly labour-intensive, this is a huge advantage. Ministry of Agriculture and Fisheries did a cost analysis comparing normal fencing to Staplelok fencing and figured out that the savings in labour more than cover the extra cost of the Staplelok system. The posts are permanent, but can be removed and re-used easily using a little stand-on jack post remover.

The Staplelok system is a world first and Kevin Joyce and his company secured international patents (which were 'bloody expensive') on the staple-locking system. In 1994 a factory in Auckland started making the system — which is selling well in the New Zealand market. Staplelok have sold the licence to manufacture the product to companies in Sweden (making fences to stop elk getting onto the roads) and in the Czech Republic, but at the moment nobody is making their fortune. The licence fees are basically covering the patent costs. Joyce is concentrating on selling further licences overseas and he is on a steep learning curve in the tricky and costly business of finding suitable foreign licencees.

Staplelok have developed a high-quality product that is more expensive than the waratah system, so Joyce is turning to the niche markets of electric security fences, vineyards, and building sites. Furthermore, the Staplelok posts and staples can be used for other applications such as hanging ceilings. A portable cattle ramp made out of Staplelok posts is another Kiwi invention which has already won an award at the Fieldays. So, like the wire which it supports, the Staplelok post is becoming an ideal new raw material for items of agricultural ingenuity.

Lifestyle farmers can do the fencing themselves with Staplelok. The posts are also colourable, so can blend in better with the environment. You could say this invention puts the traditionally Barry-Crump-and-Colin-Meads-only art of fencing within the reach of every Kiwi. This is our chance to claim our Kiwi fencing heritage! If only there was some reason to divide up and fence the backyard.

Barry Crump — a good, keen fencer.

3. KITCHEN WHIZZES

Freezer pumps, toothpicks and the largest crumpets in the world

New Zealanders have a kitchen fascination — if the world of inventions and inventors could be likened to a party, then most likely you will find a number of New Zealanders in the kitchen, re-wiring the toaster and inventing a way to break eggs without getting bits of shell in your omelette.

As we'll see in other chapters, New Zealanders have contributed to the culinary world with new recipes and innovations, but they've also given much to the science and art of food: its preparation, storage, eating, cleaning and getting bits of it out of one's teeth. From a Rongotea (small town in the Manawatu — look it up) housewife looking for a better way to freeze beans, to a multinational whiteware manufacturer looking to get a jump on their competition, New Zealand inventions in this area seem to be marked by a keenness to do things 'better', to find an improvement on existing ideas and techniques, and in the process create jobs, exports and money.

In these inventions we can start to see a pattern emerging — a good idea is part of the picture, but it must be followed with an organised and disciplined approach. All of these individuals and companies have invested heavily in their ideas: an investment of time, money and, especially, hard work. It is this, plus a good dollop of luck, which contributes to their success.

The freezer vacuum pump

Rongotea's gift to the world

If anybody is New Zealand's Kitchen Whizz, it's Norma McCulloch. Apart from being our mate Paul's aunty, she has also given the kitchen world some useful — some would say indispensable — inventions. And that's more than you can say for your aunty. Unless you're our mate Paul.

In 1968, Rongotea 'home economist' — that's housewife to you and me — Norma McCulloch was searching for a better way to avoid freezer burn. Not for herself you understand, but for her silverbeet, lamb shanks and cabbages. The basic theory is that food keeps much better in the freezer if all the air has been sucked out of the surrounding bag first. Previously, 'housewives' had been squeezing the air out of the bags by hand, or even, heaven forbid, sucking it out with a straw — a practice which, according to the admittedly self-interested McCulloch Industries, is 'warned against' by 'health authorities' and potentially dangerous.

The freezer vacuum pump was born.

My mum had one and so, probably, did yours. It consists of a cardboard (later plastic) tube, with a metal inner tube that you pump up and down vigorously. This product started as a sideline for Norma, but quickly grew to become the cornerstone of a multinational company, McCulloch Products Limited, and later McCulloch Industries Limited. At its height, the pump was sold in New Zealand, Australia, Britain, Canada and America. Son Richard came on board and led the company to bigger and better things, developing a range of products including the world's first guaranteed microwave-safe, four-piece utensil set made from space age TPX (a plastic made in Japan), lambswool chamois, non-scratch cooking utensils and even, somewhat ironically, a pump for getting air *into* balloons and Lilos. It's unclear whether the company ever went the final step and created an invention for taking air directly from freezer bags and putting into Lilos, but surely this idea was toyed with.

Not content with merely creating a range of kitchen products, the McCulloch family formed McCulloch Medical, and created a range of resuscitators and face masks. These products, similar in a way to the freezer vacuum pump, provide air to those who need it urgently, such as victims of heart attacks. It's basically a tool for giving the 'breath of life', which, probably not all too coincidentally, is what it's called. This award-winning product has been used for years by the Australian defence forces, and was used by the United Nations in Rwanda. It was designed for use with humans, but has also been adapted by veterinarians to provide a similar function for stricken animals.

Norma McCulloch demonstrating her vacuum pump to Sir Hugh Watt at the NZ High Commission, London.

The McCulloch companies are significant in size, employing New Zealand staff and contributing to our export earnings. They show what can happen when a good idea is coupled with good execution.

The BookPic toothpick

A plasticky new slant on inter-molar excavations

Consider, if you will, and I'll bet you haven't before, toothpicks. Up until recent times, this essential friend of the gap-toothed diner has been made of wood, and in restaurants either kept unhygienically in containers on the counter or expensively individually wrapped. Let's face it — it's hard to carry a toothpick with you. There probably aren't many people who, when asked, could whip out a toothpick from on their person to assist a fellow diner. As the inventor of the BookPic himself says in his United States patent application:

Toothpicks are generally provided as single items, or in containers holding a plurality of separate toothpicks. They may be of wood or synthetic plastics. It is not generally practical for an individual to carry single toothpicks in their pockets, purse, handbag, etc. The toothpicks are easily lost, readily broken, and it is not very hygienic. Furthermore, the containers for holding a plurality of toothpicks are not generally designed for personal use, but rather for offering toothpicks for use in public places, such as restaurants.

It is important that toothpicks, and especially the pick end or ends, be protected from damage. Further, where a plurality of picks are provided in a container or holder it is important that each pick be securely retained and protected in the container or holder until it is required.

Thus, it is an object of the present invention to provide toothpicks in a toothpick holder which provides a convenient personal package and which protects the toothpicks from damage, and/or which reduces or overcomes some of the above-mentioned problems, or at least which provides the public with a useful alternative.

— US Patent Application, Royce Clarke

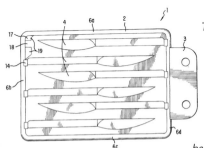

Plan from Royce Clarke's United States Patent document.

Finally, a fine Kiwi brain has developed the new toothpick. The BookPic's inventor is Royce Clarke, who gave up his property development business when his patent attorney advised him that his idea should be a full-time business. Having made a full international patent search in 1996, Royce has since patented the product internationally and has sold it to businesses in London and Denmark as well as in New Zealand.

BookPics are moulded in plastic, six to a mould, and held in a matchbook-type cardboard case. To use one, simply pull from the plastic mould. The surrounding matchbook is printed on for marketing uses with your logo or slogan, so the BookPic can be sold to restaurants, giving their customers an easy way to clean their teeth and a great reminder of their favourite eating place.

The BookPic's example shows that a great invention is a good start, but you also need a clear idea of how the invention will become a product and how that product will be marketed. The BookPic is not only a marketable product, but a product for marketing. Most importantly, though, the BookPic system is perhaps the greatest advance in toothpick technology since whittling was invented.

Royce reckons New Zealanders are natural inventors, something to do with the size and isolation of the country, and an openness to new ideas. He says many New Zealanders have ideas that they never realise are patentable. 'You have to have that belief and that gut feeling that you know it's going to be a success' — and, presumably, a predisposition for getting bits of meat caught in your molars.

World's largest crumpet maker

A serious machine for a serious bit of crumpet

Oprah Winfrey likes crumpets. You may not have known this, and we certainly didn't, but in 1994 she decided to inform all of talkshow-watching America about her breakfast favourite. Crumpets, Oprah opined, are good for you, contain fibre and carbohydrates, and were, at the time, the basis of her latest diet. ('Oprah's Crumpet a Day Diet'? 'Crumpet your way to a healthier you'? Perhaps 'Crumpets — buns of steel'?)

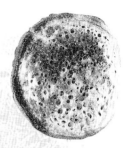

And happily she did choose to tell America, because this drove the diet-crazy Yanks to demand crumpets in such large quantities that bakeries in the States could not cope with the demand. There was a shortage of crumpetage. However, one resourceful New Zealander, Dave Garland of Auckland, when informed of the new craze in the 'craze'-iest country of them all, saw an immediate opportunity, and set out to capitalise on it.

Not one to do things by halves, Dave created the biggest crumpet maker in the world.

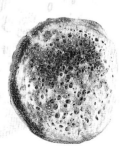

Luckily, Dave ran a commercial bakery engineering company, and he had the expertise to do it. Dave set up a deal with an American food manufacturer, and set to work creating a machine that pumps crumpets to the demanding American market. Working every hour they could for 10 weeks, including Christmas, Dave and his team of nine (including his two daughters, Ceri and Tina) completed the giant machine in time for a demonstration to his American clients that would give wheelbarrow loads of breakfast tucker for the bird life of Glenfield.

The machine produces an astounding 14,000 crumpets an hour, surely enough to keep Oprah and her fad followers well buttered for a long time to come. That's 2.35 million crumpets a week — 122 million crumpets a year! It sounds like a lot, but really it's only half a crumpet for every man, woman and child in the USA. At a cost of around half a million dollars, the machine was a sophisticated tool, with the ability to have multiple recipes and different ingredients (fancy a chocolate chip and cinnamon crumpet?), and all manufactured to exacting American standards.

When a major opportunity like this comes along, the right company with the right expertise can make a major impact — even when that company is in a small country like New Zealand. It comes down to recognising the opportunity and grabbing it.

Now I hear Phil Donaghue is quite keen on Weet-Bix....

Tullen Snips

The story of a man who had a vision of better scissors and (despite his mother's advice) ran with it

'It is amazing what you can do when you start with no preconceptions from a different angle,' says the inventor of Tullen Snips, John Hough, to which he could have added 'and when you don't really know what you are doing'.

Tullen Snips are a product familiar to a generation of New Zealanders. They burst on the scene in the late 1970s as the scissors that could cut anything, but weren't pointy, so they'd never cut you. They were in all the schools as 'Mini Snips' and achieved huge commercial success in the form of snips, as Kitchen Cutters and in a Handyman version. While scissors have been around for a long time (in fact, pivoted scissors made of iron were used by the ancient Romans) the success of Tullen Snips is due to an entirely Kiwi accident.

In 1972 somebody handed John Hough a pair of shears made overseas, suggesting he duplicate the manufacturing process and manufacture them himself. The advantage they had over normal scissors was extreme cutting power. The shears had been manufactured with a heat-treating process which hardened the steel blades. Hough set out to copy the heat-treating process, which involves dipping the steel into hot molten salts in order to try and get an even heat throughout. However, his engineers didn't really know what they were doing, and, try as they might, the process eluded them. They threw out the first 20,000 or so pairs of shears they made. The breakthrough came with an accidental result that came from not controlling the heat properly. They got what could be called a 'poor heat-treating result' but the uneven heating turned out, by pure accident, to be perfect for making shears.

Hough sent the shears to England for analysis, and the English engineers described them as having resulted from a 'very sophisticated heat-treating process'. In trying to copy an overseas product, Hough ended up with a better process for making shears. Normally the blades of shears had to be first heat-treated, then cut out, then sharpened with an expensive diamond-head sharpening process. The accidental Kiwi process meant that the steel could be punched out with a power press, then heat-treated and the resulting blades would require no sharpening!

Hough went into production with what he dubbed 'Snips'. The blades were so tough they could cut anything from paper and Glad Wrap to one-cent pieces. They were easily the most versatile home scissors in the world. The Tullen company underwent a steep learning curve in marketing, exporting, design and patent protection which led to the kitchen, children's and handyman styles of Snips and

to excellent commercial success. The wall-holder for the kitchen Snips turned out to be a more easily patented innovation than the Snips themselves, and helped battle the patent infringements of more than 100 copycat products from Taiwan and Korea.

In the days of the Muldoon Government's export incentives, Snips sold in huge volumes overseas — especially in Italy (the ancient birthplace of scissors) and in Germany. By the time John Hough sold the company and its processes and patents to Wilkinson Sword in 1985, over 20 million Snips had been shipped. The biggest single order was for 3,250,000 Snips to go out as a premium on dishwashing detergent packets in Italy.

Meanwhile, research was done with the

Tullen Snips — remember these?

Department of Education and Mini Snips were devised for the government to buy as school scissors. For a time, they were in almost every classroom in the country. Why are they no longer around? It seems Wilkinson Sword bought the Tullen company with an eye more to the processes and patents than the actual Snips product. For a time, the Penrose factory still turned out Wilkinson Sword Snips, but eventually Wilkinson Sword itself was cut up and sold off, Snips production was ceased, and a New Zealand invention faded away.

Since selling Tullen, John Hough has had only one new patent. He is looking at other ideas now, but he says the success of a patent is determined not by the idea itself, but by the perceived consumer benefit the finished product will have over other products. You can build all the better mousetraps you like, but the world will not beat a path to your door unless it's better mousetraps they want.

The Thermette

Turns the world into your kitchen

What makes the Thermette brilliant is that it is perfect. In the 60 years since it was invented, no improvements have been made to it. It has been manufactured under the same patent continuously for that whole time and it remains, as it has always been, the quickest, most efficient way to boil water in the outdoors.

WHAT A WONDERFUL XMAS PRESENT FOR DAD!! . . . .

A THERMETTE

WE GUARANTEE that it will boil sufficient water for 12 cups of tea in five minutes. It carries nearly half a gallon of water. Any Fuel may be used— PAPER, TWIGS or RUBBISH, and the More Wind the Quicker It Boils. Thermette, Large Size, in Blue or Orange finish..................10/9 each. Thermette, Large Size, Tinned Copper, N.P. finish..................35/- each. Thermette Cooking Grids, 2/3 each.

Stocked by all stores, or posted to any address in New Zealand with your Greetings enclosed, for 1/6 extra.

JOHN A. HART & CO.
PALMERSTON BLDGS., QUEEN ST., AUCKLAND.
Over 5,000 satisfied users in N.Z.

His name was John Hart (no relation to a certain ex-All Black coach) and he was originally from the Manawatu. Most of Hart's 32 other patents are now forgotten, but the Thermette, invented in 1929, caught on as standard equipment for the New Zealand troops during Second World War. The Army approached Hart to ask if he would waive the patent to help in the war effort, and he agreed. The small round scorch marks it left on the earth at first confused the German troops all over North Africa where the Thermette gained its nickname, the 'Benghazi Boiler'. Soon everyone knew the scorch marks were a sure sign that Kiwis had been there.

The Thermette can boil enough water for 12 cups of tea in just five minutes, using any old rubbish as fuel. 'The stronger the wind, the better it boils' was one of Hart's early slogans, because wind sucks air up through the conical chimney inside the boiler from the base where the fire is lit. The sucking action makes the fire roar, and the heat is transferred not only to the base of the Thermette but through the heated air rushing up the internal chimney. No heat is wasted, and that is why the Thermette is so efficient.

The original Thermette was first sold in 1931 in a blue, green and orange tin, or in tinned copper if you had a few extra bob. Kestrel Developments in Auckland are still making them to the same design. It used to be that any council workers, post workers or linemen on the side of the road could be seen setting up their Thermette, but they have largely disappeared from our roadsides. At the height of their popularity tens of thousands were made a year, now it is just a few thousand, but Trevor Tull at Kestrel Developments is hopeful for a resurgence in popularity. Its efficiency makes it an environmentally sound product, and it uses no pollutant gas, petrochemicals or hydrocarbons.

Meanwhile, the Army is still using them — at the time of writing to boil up East Timorese water. The Thermette has an official UN equipment number. Among other fans of the Thermette we can number Sam Neill, Kiwi actor, who remembers it from his youth in Central Otago: 'I learned how to stay downwind of the aromatic manuka-fuelled Thermette to avoid the sandflies.'

The Thermette has been characterised as a modest New Zealand invention that is somehow still going along, but in fact it is a brilliant piece of engineering — one of our real gifts to the world.

The Thermette — New Zealand's gift to the camping world.

4. METAL MACHINE MAN

Stamp machines, rock crushers and dishwashers

When you think of inventors and inventions, the stereotype is of a man in a workshop full of bits of metal and screws and bolts and welders, making a machine to do something. That's not all there is to the world of inventors, of course, but in New Zealand we have found it certainly is the larger part. You could invent new kinds of cheeses, unheard-of pencils, or a novel genre of songs, but we like to make machines. Whole books could feature just New Zealand machines: Barry Auckram and Bill Wilson's water-powered water heater is a self-pumping wetback-style water heater invented in Masterton in 1992. Doug Williams and Jack Humphries' 'Fluidyne Wood-Gasifier' is a generator for turning wood into electricity and has been used in remote Pacific communities. Malcolm Cooper of the South Island's Rai Valley invented a number of huge metal machines in the 1940s and '50s — a tobacco planter, a hop picker, a giant plough — all of which solved the problems that inspired them.

The stamp vending machine

A lick and a promise of wealth

In AD 60 Hero of Alexandria invented a water vending machine to sell water to thirsty people with money. In 1840 the stamp was invented in Britain. It was only a matter of time before these two inventions, racing towards each other through history, collided to form the stamp vending machine. When they did, it was a Hero of New Zealand who brought them together.

It occurred to RJ Dickie, while working at the front desk in a Wellington Post Office in 1891, at the age of 15, that a machine should be able to tear stamps off and hand them to people and save him from doing it. When Dickie saw his first moving picture images he reasoned that stamps should be able to be handled just like photographs strung together. He began to plan, and over the next several years the idea underwent gestation. Finally the invention was due. 'For some months, the idea of a machine to sell postage

Dickie and his stamp machine.

stamps (by means of a coin in the slot) became an obsession with me. I kept banishing the idea from coming into being, but at last the urge would not let me sleep, and for peace of mind I started working on the making of the model.'

At age 28, Dickie (because he was hopeless at drawing) roped in a couple of helpers — draughtsman JH Brown and engineer W Andrews and together they designed, built and patented the first ever stamp vending machine in the world. It wasn't very big — the mechanism being only nine by four inches. A fluted sprocket wheel with weights attached was set in motion by the descending coin so as to make a single stamp project from a slot.

Several American machines had been attempted already, but Dickie's had a superior mechanism. The American machines were impractical because they were heavy, expensive and had a very limited stamp-holding capacity. Dickie's major innovations were the fact that the falling coin caused the stamp to be ejected without pulling a lever or turning a wheel, and that the stamps were stored in a roll. The roll of stamps had been used before on machines to fix stamps automatically to multiple envelopes but never for a vending machine. The Dickie patent was also licensed later to make machines for dispensing tram and theatre tickets.

On 15 June 1905 the first public trial took place and a Wellingtonian (whose name remains unrecorded) was the first person to buy a stamp from a vending machine in the vestibule of the Chief Post Office. It was an immediate success and sold 3902 stamps in 14 days before another feat of Kiwi ingenuity brought the trial to an end. Someone had figured out that you didn't need to use a penny, just something that was shaped like a penny, and had scored some free stamps. Some modifications were required.

Dickie's invention was an international success. The time was just right, as demand for stamps was high, as was the interest in the convenience of vending machines. A year after the first machine proved itself, Dickie travelled overseas, taking his machine with him on a business trip for the Post Office. In 1907, to get the British to cotton on to the idea, he set up a machine in the lobby of the House of Commons. It was a popular curiosity. A story from the *Dominion* at the time of Dickie's death states that, 'Frock-coated members stopped and stared as they passed through the lobby... like children at the fair, the venerable Edwardians could not resist the temptation to try out the world's first practical stamp-selling machine.'

The marketing ploy worked and the British government began to

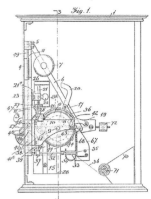

Dickie's vending machine — the best in the world for half a century.

manufacture the machines. Soon the New Zealand stamp vending machine was being manufactured all over the world under licence from Dickie. In fact, by the time the New Zealand government decided they wanted some more, in 1909, they could already import them from Britain. Meanwhile, in the same year at the Alaska–Yukon–Pacific Exposition in Seattle, the vending machine won the Gold Medal, Grand Prize and Diploma against all comers.

Dickie kept updating his designs as time went on and his stamp vending machines were manufactured all over the world for 50 years. Just after the First World War, the company that was manufacturing the machines had orders for over 100,000 — orders they couldn't fill. Dickie once visited a factory in England where 800 men were making machines from his design. By 1938 some 18,000 had been installed in Britain alone! We can only assume that, although he never quit his job at the Post Office, Dickie was made at least comfortably, if not filthy, rich by his invention.

For half a century Dickie was the world king of stamp vending. Finally his machines began to be superseded — when postal rates began to change rapidly in the 1960s, it proved difficult for the Dickie machine to keep up. But the real death knell was sounded by dirty vandals! There are no stamp vending machines left operating in New Zealand today, because of the sad fact that hooligans would smash them.

The Barmac rock crusher

Breaking rocks not so bad after all

It used to be that breaking rocks was seen as a punishment for criminals, but it's been anything but for two New Zealand inventors.

Jim McDonald had had a distinguished career in the Navy during and after the Second World War, winning the DSO and DSC, both with bars, and inventing a number of pieces of useful naval equipment. Among his inventions for the Navy were a new type of slide rule and a device for firing torpedoes abreast, rather than one after the other. After leaving the Navy he turned his inventiveness to more public works, literally. McDonald became an engineer for the Wellington City Council, and in 1970 began work on a new rock-crushing machine for the quarry in the Ngauranga Gorge.

Make Barmac your Kiwi rock crusher of choice.

Bryan Bartley was also an engineer, who at that time worked for Winstones, and when he came across McDonald and his nascent machine he recognised a great idea that needed further refining ('scuse the pun), but with the potential to be very big. Thus Bartley and McDonald began a long-term business partnership, and a friendship that would last many years.

The crushing machine they came up with was born of the idea that the most efficient way to crush rocks was not to bang them against steel, or grip them in a vise — the two prevailing techniques at the time. Each of these ways had the major problem of wear and tear: over quite a short time the action of the rocks against the steel would wear the parts away. McDonald and Bartley's machine used the action of rocks against rocks, and so reduced drastically the wear and tear on the machine.

Basically the machine they came up with — dubbed the 'Barmac crusher' (you can work out why) — relied on two facts which they recognised: stones will break if you bang them together hard enough, and steel will be protected from the abrasion if it is covered with a layer of rocks. The parts of the machine that did have to grate against the rocks were replaced with tungsten, and the Barmac crusher became one of the most efficient and popular crushers on the market.

Rock crushing — believe it ore (sic) not — is big business. McDonald and Bartley saw their machine being used in the creation of aggregate (small rocks) for roading, but it also became a huge deal in the mining industry, where even today the Barmac machine is the crusher of choice. It took eight years to turn their idea into a viable business, but the success of the product soon saw Bartley and McDonald licensing its manufacture around the world. They sold the business in 1990 to a Swedish company, who continue to manufacture the Barmac in Matamata.

Unfortunately McDonald died in 1982, but it seems Bartley can't shake the inventive spirit. After selling the Barmac he has gone on to help develop another Kiwi invention, the 'kiwifeather prop™', a self-feathering propeller for boaties.

Two-drawer dishwasher

Why have one dishwasher when you can have two?

I think we'd all agree that Fisher & Paykel is a household name. This large manufacturer of whiteware has been part of New Zealanders' lives since it was first formed in 1934,

Fisher and Paykel decided to bring you a drawer each.

although it wasn't until 1960 that they started manufacturing their own designs. Fisher & Paykel have created a number of innovations, including the ECM motor — basically a clever electronic motor with programmable software built in. This motor has formed part of a number of Fisher & Paykel products, and led to them creating the two-drawer dishwasher.

A dishwasher with drawers, I hear you exclaim...why? Well, why not? It's a simple extension to the 'standard' dishwasher, but on reflection offers a number of advantages — dishes can be separated, you can put only one drawer on if that's all that's needed, and the two drawers can be placed apart nicely in your designer kitchen and operated independently. Apparently the technology is already very popular with the elderly in the United States, who, it seems, are reluctant to start the dishwasher when it's only half full.

The two drawers have different uses: a smaller drawer is designed for fast washing of small loads — glassware, cups and mugs, perhaps crumpet-stained breakfast dishes — and a larger drawer for utensils, pots and pans, that sort of thing. No longer do fine crystal glasses have to slum it with the filthy lasagne-covered oven dish; in this new class system of cleanliness they can have their own separate abode. And thanks to Fisher & Paykel, who knows how far this segregation of washing may go? Perhaps next on the horizon is the two-part clothes washer — a separation of whites and coloureds in some kind of clothing apartheid?

Head of the engineering team at Fisher & Paykel is company director Julian Williams, an aeronautical engineer by training who wanted to work at Cape Canaveral. (You don't have to be a rocket scientist to work for Fisher & Paykel, but it does help.) It was his team that led the company to create this revolution in automated platter scouring, and create an entirely new market segment in the process.

The two-drawer dishwasher is contributing to the $700-million-a-year company's future, and is also, by the way, a hit with the Jewish community in the United States, whose kosher rules require them to separate meat and dairy products and utensils.

Fisher & Paykel don't just sell whiteware; they also supply a range of medical equipment, including air humidifiers for hospitals based on their motor. With over 3000 staff in New Zealand, the company is a good example of just how far a good idea can take you — and how many filthy dishes there are.

World's first fully automated soft-serve ice cream vending machine

Stopping ice cream wastage

When you next go to your favourite fast-food restaurant and get a soft-serve ice cream, chances are that the person serving you will give you too much. Up to 25 percent too much — good for you, tubby, but not so good for the fast-food company. Finding an accurate way to measure the amount of ice cream given out has been a problem hounding the fast food industry since Ronald McDonald first put on make-up and started flogging Happy Meals.

Enter Industrial Research Limited (IRL), a name you'll come across a number of times throughout the book. They were assembled from the former government department known as the DSIR (Department of Scientific and Industrial Research). On this occasion they were allied with a Hamilton-based company, Blue Boy International. IRL had been working on a project creating a sensitive gripper mechanism for food handling when Blue Boy made them aware of the problem.

According to Bernie Cook, managing director of Blue Boy, soft-serve ice cream is a tough substance to deal with because it's not quite a solid, nor a liquid. Luckily the IRL gripper project provided the techno savvy needed and the problem could be satisfactorily solved. The finished machine uses an 'expert system' — computer software designed to feed back information to ensure the exact proportions are reached no matter who is using it. The potential for the product is enormous, and in 1998 it won the supreme award of the Foodtech innovation awards at the Foodtech exhibition in Auckland.

A consumer oblivious to sensitive gripper mechanisms.

5. WEIRD SCIENCE

DNA, black holes and seismic shock absorbers

Why are our internationally famous mathematicians obscure in their own country? Maybe it's simply because there are no famous brands of mathematics, mathematics is not an Olympic event, and maths isn't on the telly. Maybe if the nation succumbed to a week of mourning after losing a maths match to the French, then our mathematicians would be big names. But it is because maths lies behind the science which lies behind everyday life that it is at once so important, and so obscure to general observation.

In science, as well as in maths, New Zealand has made some valuable contributions. The people discussed here are inventors as much as any others in this book. We believe it is worth the effort of attempting to understand in at least a simple way what it was that these people have done, so as to get a more holistic picture of New Zealand inventions on the world stage. And rest assured that the mathematical achievements of the following New Zealanders are each things that no South African, Australian or Pom ever managed, although the story does start with a Swiss/German.

The Kerr metric

The mathematics of rotating black holes

In 1930 Albert Einstein, a patent clerk in Switzerland, started work on his 'Theory of General Relativity'. In 1963, Roy Kerr, a university professor in New Zealand, finished it.

Well, kind of.

When Einstein penned his revolutionary theory, he left a number of 'holes'. It was later discovered that these holes were quite literally holes — stellar phenomena that you have probably heard referred to as 'black holes'. These were initially thought so weird and exotic that they couldn't exist 'in the real world', but over time scientists came to realise that, not only did they exist in the cosmos, but they are quite common, with one even at the heart of our own galaxy.

Black holes are basically very heavy 'things', so heavy that their gravitational pull is strong enough to suck in everything which comes close to them, even light — and it can't escape. They eat up everything around them, and given that they are so incredibly heavy (a teaspoon of the stuff would be many times heavier than the whole Earth), they distort space and time in the surrounding area. It's basically like having really bad neighbours who bring down the entire neighbourhood. It is in the study of this 'neighbourhood' that Professor Kerr made his contribution. In fact, to be entirely accurate, it's the study of rotating black holes, so it's kind of like neighbours who bring down the neighbourhood and at the same time spin at incredible speeds. Maybe our whole neighbourhood metaphor is kind of falling apart, but then so does the fabric of space around a black hole, so it's kind of appropriate.

What Kerr did was to sit down and write some very complex equations which model very accurately what goes on near a black hole. Scientists use Kerr's equations to guess what black holes might do as they pass through space, and science fiction writers ignore Kerr's equations when they make spaceships fly into them and arrive in another dimension. If Arthur C Clarke had just done his maths, that whole *2001: A Space Odyssey*

thing would never have happened.

From the time of Kerr's announcement of his theory, it proved to be an enormously useful way of describing what scientists call 'spacetime'. The 'Kerr metric', as it became known, is still the method used to examine the complex geometry of the region surrounding black holes.

For completeness, and to prove we've done our research, we've included the equation for the Kerr metric written in Boyer-Lindquist co-ordinates. So what does it all mean? We have no idea. We'd venture to suggest you don't either, but we don't think this makes Kerr's innovation any less important or noteworthy. If we all understood it then someone else would probably have already thought of it and we'd have nothing for this bit of the book.

Seismic isolators

Shock absorbers for buildings

In an earthquake, to completely state the obvious, things move around a lot. Huge towers of mirror glass hang precariously above the main streets of virtually every city on Earth, and the vulnerability of high-rise buildings to earthquakes is a major factor in their success or failure — too often sub-standard buildings entomb thousands of unfortunates when big earthquakes hit.

Rightly or wrongly, as Kiwis, we see ourselves as sort of international earthquake

The Kerr metric

$$ds^2 = -a^2 dt^2 + \omega^2(d\phi - \omega dt)^2 + (\rho^2/\Delta)dr^2 + \rho^2 d\theta^2$$

where the co-ordinate functions are given (with $G = c = 1$):

$$\Delta = r + a^2 - 2Mr$$
$$\Sigma^2 = (r^2 + a^2)^2 - a^2\Delta \sin^2\theta$$
$$\rho^2 = r^2 + a^2 \cos^2\theta$$

$$\omega = \frac{\Sigma}{\rho} \sin\theta$$

the specific angular momentum is:

$$a = \frac{GJ}{Mc^3}, 0 \leq a \leq 1$$

Incidentally, the physical value of J is for a star like our sun:

$$J = 1.63 \times 10^{48} \, gcm^2/s$$

Corresponding to $a = 0.185$ M. If $a = 0$ we have the Schwarzschild case for a non-rotating black hole (or star).

So there!

Bill Robinson's seismic isolators (top) ensure both Te Papa (above) and Parliament Buildings (right) are earthquake-proof.

experts. Napier, Murchison, Inangahua, Edgecumbe. We are quite proud of the precarious position of our capital on a major fault line. In fact we are so proud of our fault lines, that we should rename them our 'good point' lines. Whether or not we actually have more experience of earthquakes than most places, it was certainly a Kiwi who invented one of the most important measures to make cities safer in their event. Dr Bill Robinson came up with the idea of 'shock absorbers' for buildings. More importantly, he also came up with a way to make them. Robinson led a team of scientists at the then DSIR (now Industrial Research Limited — that's progress for you) to invent these 'seismic shock absorbers'.

Basically the shock absorbers are rubber and steel rings surrounding a whole pile of lead plates, put at the base of buildings like piles to hold the building up. For most of the time, they sit there quietly, hoisting the building up with little or no fanfare. Then, suddenly and without warning, bang! An earthquake hits. It might be downtown LA in January 1994 and this might be the building at the University of Southern California Teaching Hospital, say.

The ground moves beneath the building from side to side and, given the tremendous weight of the building above, the top can't move as quickly. The building is under immense pressure to 'shear' — physics-speak for 'move sideways a bit too much'. But the sheer shear pressure of the building above compresses down on one side of the shock absorber, and a weird thing happens. The lead at the core melts for an instant, taking the pressure of the building above and the ground below. It 'gives'. Then, as the shock passes, the rubber and steel rings snap the lead back into shape, where it reforms an instant later. In physics terms the lead undergoes a plastic transformation. This phenomenon is fairly uncommon, but luckily lead displays exactly the behaviour needed by Robinson and his team. Incidentally, the same property of lead has helped keep the Parthenon in Greece standing for thousands of years.

The shock absorbers are a great success. Many thousands of them are in place worldwide, protecting hundreds of millions of dollars of buildings, from the LA Teaching Hospital to New Zealand's own Parliament Buildings, the Tokyo Post Office and the Wellington CPO. Indeed, Te Papa, our national museum, stands where it is today on Dr Robinson's shock absorbers. It's handy stuff, lead. Next time you have a difficult handyman-type problem to solve around the house, why not stop for a second to consider whether or not the plasticity of lead under shock could lead to a solution....

Exposing DNA

The blueprint of life hails from Pongaroa

When the King of Sweden presented the 1962 Nobel Prize for Medicine, he didn't just give it to those limelight-hogging scientists, JD Watson and Francis Crick. There was a third recipient, who seems to be often forgotten, and was none other than New Zealander Maurice Wilkins.

Watson and Crick's contribution to the understanding of deoxyribonucleic acid is well heralded, and I would guess were you to ask any reasonably educated person who discovered DNA, theirs would be the names put forward. There is a good reason for this: for a long time the idea of the 'double helix' structure of DNA, and its role in life, was referred to as the 'Watson-Crick' conjecture, after the two scientists who basically guessed it first. But it wasn't until Maurice Wilkins had done an awful lot of work that the proposal was accepted as fact. In short, Wilkins 'proved' the conjecture.

Maurice Wilkins was born in Pongaroa (north-east of Masterton) in 1916, but moved to England fairly early on in life to be educated. He studied for years, getting his PhD in 1940 for work involving phosphorescence, and then during the war turned his efforts to solving problems such as the improvement of radar screens. He worked for a while separating uranium isotopes, and did a stint working for the infamous 'Manhattan Project' in California, until the return of peace in 1945 saw him return to his studies.

He worked for many years after the war on the study of various chemicals and structures in cells, honing his techniques and methods until in the late 1950s he began X-ray diffraction studies of DNA and sperm heads.

Maurice Wilkins – the unsung hero of DNA.

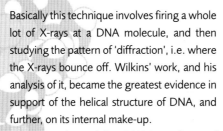

Basically this technique involves firing a whole lot of X-rays at a DNA molecule, and then studying the pattern of 'diffraction', i.e. where the X-rays bounce off. Wilkins' work, and his analysis of it, became the greatest evidence in support of the helical structure of DNA, and further, on its internal make-up.

Wilkins showed that DNA is made up of two tiny fibres coiled around each other in a spiral shape — a helix. If you could see them close up they would look like a spiral staircase. The links between the two strands — the 'stairs' in this analogy — are molecules of chemicals called amino acids. Surprisingly, there are only a few of these different amino acids in the DNA. In human DNA there are only four: adenine, cytosine, guanine and thymine, commonly known by single letters, A, C, G and T. Even more surprisingly, the amino acids can only link to each other in one way, with G and C, and T and A always paired.

It is something as simple as the order in which these four amino acids occur that leads to the huge variety of life around us. Where in your DNA structure, in the part that codes for, say, eye colour, you may have the amino acid pattern GCCGCTAGCCCG which might lead to brown eyes, I'll have GAATCCGGATAT, which makes my eyes blue. Of course, these aren't the real patterns, they're probably a lot more complex (the DNA 'formula' for a human being takes about 3×10^9 of these patterns), but in a simple sense this is what Watson, Crick and Wilkins showed.

Temperature-calibrating devices

Exactly how cold is it?

Industrial Research Limited, a company assembled from the former DSIR, have made a number of contributions to the study of science and technology, and their name crops up again and again throughout this book. Here we're looking at an award-winning device created by IRL scientist Rod White that basically tells you if your electronic thermometer is any good for the modest sum of $4000.

OK, OK, so the thermometer was invented a long time ago, and Jim Hickey can tell you the temperature for nothing every night on the news, but what makes Rod White's device so special is that it is accurate to a few millionths of a degree. I can't see Jim letting us know that 'the 3 o'clock high today in New Plymouth was 29.4512 degrees Celsius....'

So apart from obsessive meteorologists, who needs to know the temperature so accurately? Quite a lot of scientific and technical work, and even some industrial processes, are critically dependent on the exact temperature, and it's not always necessarily so far removed from everyday life. For instance, measuring the temperature-dependent properties of airline fuel is critical, and mistakes of even a tiny amount in the laboratory can result in high-altitude catastrophes.

Making sure everyone uses the same

standards of measure has been a continuing struggle for science and trade, and led to the establishment of an international measurement standards laboratory in Paris in the late 1800s. Nowadays the laboratory co-ordinates the world's national standards laboratories to make sure all our measurements — such as the metre, the litre and the second — are the same wherever you measure them. With temperature things can be a little easier, as temperature scales are defined by the melting points and freezing points of various metals — measuring these (at fixed pressures) is reasonably easy, and then the task becomes estimating the temperatures in the 'gaps' between the known points. For instance, 0 degrees and 100 degrees Celsius were originally defined as the temperatures at which water freezes and boils at sea level. The temperature between these points is divided into 100 to make degrees (Latin for 'steps').

What Rod White's machine does is to use a simple network of electrical resistors — with some devious electrical tricks and an old mathematical theorem — to check the instruments that measure the gaps. His machine is actually designed to calibrate other temperature-measuring devices — a kind of 'temperature-taker audit'. In the past this could only be done using extremely expensive machines, of which there were only three or four in the world. It was the combination of tricks Rod used that was innovative, and the

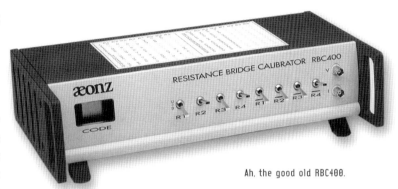

Ah, the good old RBC400.

same combination of tricks can be used to check a wide range of measuring instruments, not just thermometers. Rod White's invention means measurement labs across the world can improve their standards.

Knot theory

Doughnuts and coffee cups give a Kiwi the Fields Medal

The Fields Medal is often referred to as the 'Nobel Prize' of mathematics. Mathematics, interestingly enough (to mathematicians anyway), does not have a Nobel Prize per se, but the Fields Medal has the same kind of prestige as the Nobel. It is only awarded to four people per year worldwide, for significant contributions to the study of mathematics. The only New Zealander ever to receive one is Dr Vaughan Jones, born in Gisborne, who received his for work done in the mathematical area called topology.

Topology is a branch of mathematics regarding shapes. It is often called 'rubber sheet geometry', but this has nothing to do with mathematicians' propensity for bed-wetting. Rather, it's the idea that in topology shapes are defined not by their geometric shapes but by their complexity. Thus a circle and a triangle in two-space are topologically identical (neither containing holes and so being equally complex), so too are doughnuts and a coffee cup in three-space — maths language for 'the real world'. Don't worry, it's pretty esoteric stuff, and like a lot of pure mathematics, actually more resembles gibberish than it does plain English ('*Let M denote a von Neumann algebra. Then M is an algebra of bound operators acting on a Hilbert space H....*')

Like many others at the top of their fields, Jones left New Zealand after his initial studies and went to work and study in a variety of countries and universities. Always, though, it seems Jones typified the New Zealand spirit — he has been described as 'informal' and 'encouraging the free and open exchange of ideas'. In the admirable tradition of mathematicians, he often gives out details of what he is working on to allow others to contribute their thoughts and ideas, not jealously guarding his own ideas to hog all the glory.

When Jones was awarded his medal in 1990, it was specifically for the discovery of a new relationship within the realm he was studying, a 'polynomial invariant' that apparently had been missed by many others who were studying in the same area. This is akin to a whole lot of gold prospectors working the same stretch of river when one of them strikes gold. In this case, the gold was due to hard work and inspiration as much as luck.

Jones' Fields Medal was in recognition of him as an inventor of mathematical machines, an engineer making things out of numbers. As a nice finale, apparently Dr Jones caused quite a stir in 1990 when he attended the International Mathematics Congress to pick up his prize, giving his valedictory lecture dressed in the All Black rugby strip. I wonder what number he had on his back. Probably not 2 or 15; more likely

$$\sqrt{\frac{i^2}{2}}$$

$$(a+b)^2 \times y(4^a - y^x) > 3\pi^4 \times 6(b + 3^y \times 7t)$$
$$\sqrt{6 \times b}$$
$$(4\cos xy^x r + 10^6(x \times d^2 - t(\omega-5)) \times 4 - 3^x$$
$$29\sqrt[4]{6.4321}(b^4 \times 9^{10})^a < \pi^6 - 4(9^x \times 8ab^2)\frac{2^3}{3t}$$
$$(94\ 3.1 \times a) - (tb^3 \times x^{4.1})$$
$$\frac{32b \times 9t^x}{43x^2} - (39ab) < \pi(9^{!} \times v \qquad ab^x$$
$$t^4 \times 2(b^9 x \times 4\sqrt{6.111} - \quad > \qquad -10)$$
$$\left\{ \begin{array}{l} at^2 \times 4(9^a \times 4 - 6^t) \\ 49\sqrt{910} < 3.169^a \\ \overline{92^t} \end{array} \right\} y^4 \times 9t\, b^x (4t, \omega^a, y^2)$$

And I hear the All Blacks often reciprocate by holding coffee cups and eating doughnuts.

KiwiStar

Ultra sharp photos

Like many of us in 1986, David Beach stood outside his home at night in the cold, looking skyward for a glimpse of Halley's comet. And like many of us, he was disappointed in this 'once in a lifetime' event — imagination played quite a large part in the proceedings. Beach tried photographing the comet, but again with disappointing results. The comet was too far away, and the light from it was too dim.

But, unlike the rest of us, Dr David Beach was a physicist working for the Industrial Research Limited's Imaging and Sensing division, with training and experience in refraction techniques and optics. He set about creating what was to become an incredibly powerful lens system.

Beach was born in England and began his career as a scientist there, working for many years in atomic weapons research, before moving to New Zealand in 1973 to work with the then DSIR. He's had an incredibly varied scientific career, studying everything from high power lasers, to breast cancer, to the measurement of fat of the backs of sheep. He has even published works on lunar dynamics and Stonehenge, but with the establishment of IRL he moved into the study and application of optics.

This man may be watching you.

The KiwiStar system is a new type of ultra-fast camera lens with high resolution, broad spectral bandpass and high scalability (100 mm to greater than 2 m), which has no low-order aberrations. In terms we all can understand, it's a very high quality lens that can take crystal clear pictures over a long distance. A lens system of this quality has application in many areas, from astronomy, where it can be used to study stars from Earth with great precision, to surveillance — the KiwiStar lens can photograph a car number plate from a kilometre away at night, making it an ideal tool for police and the military.

IRL have patented the system, and now it is available for licence worldwide, so it seems only a matter of time before the KiwiStar system finds widespread use. And maybe in 2056, when Halley's comet arcs its way back into view, we'll all be able to have a good close-up look, thanks to Dr Beach.

6. DAIRY ME

Milking machines, spreadable butter, and a high-frequency cheese cutter

It will come as no surprise to any of us that New Zealand has made some real contributions to new ideas and inventions in the dairy industry. It would be fair to say a good proportion of our country's economy still revolves around the udder, and our lush pastures are perfect for good quality milk and its by-products.

All that hands-on time in the shed and dairy factory has resulted in plenty of improvements in extracting milk from the cow and doing things with it (the milk) afterwards.

The Vacreator

Taking the stink out of butter

The Vacreator looks much more impressive in colour.

Butter smells bad. We just don't know it. And the people the world has to thank for our blissful, odourless ignorance are New Zealanders Lamont Murray and Frank Board.

In 1923 Lamont and Board were about to open their own butter factory in Te Aroha, and were unhappy about the method that was being used to pasteurise the cream for the butter. Back then the cream was quite contaminated with outside flavours, things that the cow may have been eating that found their way into the milk — some kinds of feed and even weeds. Pasteurisation basically involved boiling the cream and cooling it again. This may have killed all the bad things in the cream, but it didn't help it to smell or taste better — it was common for cream to come out of the process tasting cooked or even burnt.

Quite apart from the aesthetic, there were financial and economic reasons to improve the process too. Firstly, the government at the time had regulated it so that suppliers were to be paid on the quality of the cream delivered to the factory, meaning farmers and suppliers had great incentive to improve their product. Secondly, poor quality cream results in poor quality butter, and this was a time when New Zealand butter was beginning to be exported in large quantities to England. The poor quality stuff not only didn't last as well on the trip, but it didn't sell for as much.

Murray and Board were a perfect team to combat the problem. Murray came from a family of milk producers and manufacturers, while Board's family were involved in importing and marketing New Zealand and Australian butter into England. Once they opened their factory together in Te Aroha they began to immediately concentrate on how to make their end product better. They made some evolutionary improvements to the current processes, and these gave encouraging results — in today's language, it went straight to the bottom line — and this encouraged them to seek further improvements.

By 1933 they had done it. They had come up with a technique for deodorising cream that had no side effects. Basically the technique involved passing hot steam through the cream instead of boiling it. This was quite a novel concept at the time, as conventional wisdom frowned upon the use of steam, but Murray and Board came up with a way of making it work, and created a series of machines to assist in the process — machines they dubbed the 'Vacreator'.

The Vacreator was a great success. Murray and Board set up a company to manufacture and license the concept, and it was quickly adopted and used in New Zealand. Board travelled to the United States during the 1930s and succeeded in converting the dairy industry there to the techniques the Vacreator offered, diversifying its uses to suit the larger American market.

'Improvements in and relating to milking apparatus'

The most overused phrase at the New Zealand patent office

It used to be, that if you wanted milk from a cow, you got down there with a bucket and milked it by hand. No problem if you just wanted a quick drink, or to feed the family, but as a commercial exercise it was dismal. When it takes, say, five minutes to milk a cow by hand, and you've got 25 of them to do, twice a day, that's over four hours of back-breaking work, huddled in a cold milking shed. There had to be a better way.

And, of course there was. Mechanised milking apparatus first came to the market in about 1900, though by all accounts these first machines offered little improvement on the old ways. The earliest machine took 20 minutes to milk a cow, but it did milk two at a time, and it

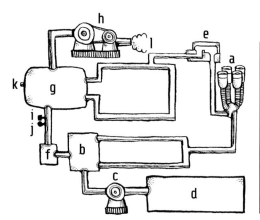

John Blake's Simplex Milker.

a	milking unit
b	receiver jar
c	milk pump
d	bulk tank
e	pulsator
f	sanitary trap
g	reserve tank
h	vacuum pump
i	regulator
j	guage
k	automatic drain
l	exhaust line

No invention yet for avoiding that irksome 'milk moustache'.

saved one bending over for the whole process. Some of the early machines had cups that would attach to the cow's teats, and then not come off again! The teats would swell and the poor cow would be stuck, until the farmer loosened a rubber band on the top of the cup. Most unsatisfactory.

One farmer who worked through this was John Blake, of Taranaki. Blake ran dairy cows in the early 20th century, and was obviously a bit of a technophile, an early adopter of technology. He bought one of the earliest milking machines, but quickly realised its limitations. In true Kiwi spirit, and thanks to his training as an engineer, he set about improving the machine, redesigning the cups so a cow was milked in a quarter of the time.

Word got around, and Blake's neighbours asked him to create improved cups for their machines too, which Blake did happily, the extra money supplementing the farm income. However, after having made a half a dozen sets the manufacturers of the original machine discovered what Blake was doing. Instead of congratulating him on his initiative and purchasing the design from him, they claimed his 'improvement' was an infringement of their patent rights, and forced him not only to purchase back all the cups he'd made for his neighbours, but to cease using the design on his own machine!

Rightly annoyed, Blake took the opportunity to design and create an entire milking machine of his own from scratch, a process he finished in 1907 when he sold his first 'Simplex Milker'. Blake's new design was even better than his first, using an overhead pulsator, and the machine was simpler and more efficient than any around. Farmers came from miles around to see the machine in action, and eventually Blake gave up dairy farming to concentrate on selling his milker. Then in 1910 he sold his patent rights, and the machine began to be marketed worldwide.

Other Kiwi inventors took up the challenge, and creating improvements to milking machines became a national pastime. Sidney Knapp, a Greytown dairy farmer in the 1920s, was quite an inventor too. His 'improved hoisting apparatus', 'petrol-saving engine' and most notably the 'Knapp sack sprayer' — a back-pack flame thrower unit — were among the inventions pertaining to milking. Like Blake, he started out by improving elements of the machine, using his steam engineer's skills to patent an 'improvement to milking valves' in 1921. And then, like Blake, he went on to create an entirely new milking machine.

Nowadays most patents relating to milking are registered by companies, but there are still one or two individual inventors, working away in their milking sheds, who keep coming up with good ideas to make their lives easier, and in the process create 'improvements in and relating to milking apparatus'.

Spreadable butter

No more ripped toast

In the great debates of humanity — cloth nappies v. disposables, manual cars v. automatic, folders v. scrunchers — it is the margarine v. butter debate that surely must have most ardent followers. Are you a marg eater or a butter admirer? There's no sitting on the fence in this debate — you know what you are.

Not wanting to display any bias or impartiality in this debate, I won't state which I am, but I think it's true to say that in this debate those bloody marg lovers have always had the killer argument. No, not cholesterol, not price, not even, laughably, taste. The killer argument for the marg camp has always been 'Yes, but can you spread it on your toast?' And, of course, they've been right. In the past it was necessary to keep the butter out of the fridge, or bung it in the hot water cupboard for a while just to get it to a spreadable consistency. But now, thanks to the New Zealand Dairy Research Institute, you can wipe, or rather spread, that self-righteous, polyunsaturated grin off their faces.

The New Zealand Dairy Research Institute staff started working on the 'spreadable butter' project in the 1970s, but it took until 1990 to get a viable commercial plant off the ground. In the meantime a group of dedicated butter admirers had to work out a way to use the same raw materials as 'normal' butter — cream and salt — to make a spreadable butter. They determined that the secret is not what

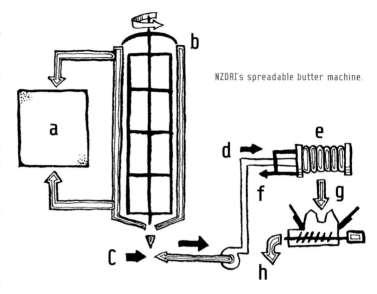

NZDRI's spreadable butter machine.

a	temperature control system
b	crystalliser
c	milk fat from fresh cream to crystalliser
d	crystal slurry to filter
e	filter
f	soft fractions
g	hard fractions
h	hard fractions

you put in, it's what you take out.

Butter contains a large number of different types of — and I hesitate to use this word for fear of giving ammunition to the margarine supporters, but it is the chemically correct term — fatty acids or 'triglycerides'. Now some of these triglycerides have melting points in the same range as the difference in temperature between the fridge and the room. In other words, when butter is in the fridge these triglycerides are frozen, making the butter hard, but if you leave it out of the fridge they melt, making the butter runnier. The NZDRI team correctly surmised that if they could somehow remove these particular triglycerides, leaving everything else intact, then the butter should be the same consistency at fridge temperature as it is at room temperature.

Doing it on a small scale wasn't much of a problem. Doing it on the scale needed for commercial production was a bit more of a challenge, but the team managed it, and in 1990 the world's first spreadable butter oozed off the production lines. But not onto *our* supermarket shelves. It seems the problem of hard butter was not initially considered severe enough in New Zealand to warrant selling here — apparently New Zealand is one of the few countries in the world where fridges have butter conditioners in them, keeping the butter warmer than the rest of the fridge. So for the first six or seven years of its creamy-textured existence, all our spreadable butter went offshore.

In England it was an immediate hit, with sales rocketing. In 1998 in England spreadable butter was the fastest growing grocery product, with sales increasing by 37 percent.

But with success comes jealousy, and it came in 1996 in the form of a punitive levy on the import of New Zealand spreadable butter into the European Communities, with those, obviously marg-loving, EC officials claiming that spreadable butter did not meet the strict criteria for importation of New Zealand butter under the preferential tariff, as it wasn't 'manufactured directly from milk or cream'. This was pure hogwash, and the decision was overturned in 1999 as a result of action taken by New Zealand against the EC within the World Trade Organisation.

Spreadable butter was of course released in New Zealand too, and became as big a hit here as it was overseas. We can thank the team at the NZDRI for the ease with which we can now butter our toast in the mornings, and the vanquishing of the margarine foe. Of course the guys that make the butter conditioners are ropable.

The high-frequency cheese cutter

It was these guys who cut the cheese

Now you and I probably have no truck with the way cheese is cut. We go through our cheese-cutting lives, slicing away at the block, creating uneven-sized pieces to our heart's content. Likewise, when we go to the supermarket to buy our 1 kg block of cheddar, it would only be the most anally retentive among us who whip out the scales and check just whether or not we are getting exactly what we are paying for.

But that's what differentiates we consumers from the producers of the products we buy. Those producers do care; they care very much. Commercial experience shows that cutting inaccuracies in commercial plants can leave cheese blocks as much as 15 percent overweight. This of course has an impact on the producers, and they're not happy. The major problem is that cheese is quite a difficult substance to cut accurately. That is, until an innovative Kiwi technology firm, Ryan Manufacturing, came along.

Ryan Manufacturing saw the problem and came up with a high-tech solution. They had already worked out a system of creating high-frequency energy waves, and could see an application for this technology in the cheese-cutting problem. Basically, if they could make a machine where the blade moves fast enough, they should be able to create an incredibly accurate cut. However, before their idea could be turned into commercial reality, they had to solve some problems.

Ryan got together with the University of Waikato, and a graduate student Tom (Qi) Zimang. The idea was for Tom to work on the problem Ryan had — to do with translating the high-energy waves into the blade's cutting motion — and in the process the work would count for his doctoral thesis. The collaboration was a great success.

The machine Ryan came up with, with Tom Zimang's assistance, had a blade that can vibrate at 20 kilohertz — 20,000 times per second! That's an incredible rate, and it meant the actual 'blade' didn't need to be sharp at all — indeed, the blade resembles the back of a normal knife.

The dairy giant Anchor, not scared off by the — literally — cutting edge technology, purchased the first model from Ryan Manufacturing, and it is in use today in their factory, cutting 20 kg blocks of cheese into smaller ones of 1 kg and 500 g. The machine takes just 12 seconds to process an entire 20 kg block. The machine is now accurate to within 1 percent of the weight, and Anchor can now get 36 individual 500 g blocks out of a 20 kg block, much better for them than the 33 they used to get. The machine is worth its weight in, if not gold, then surely at least cheese.

Ryan are excited by the future of the technology they spent over two years developing, and see the big opportunity being offshore sales. Like many small New Zealand companies, they acknowledge that marketing is their weakness — a weakness they are starting to overcome as they look to expand.

The application of their idea of high frequency cutting does not, of course, end with cheese. They've already been looking into its uses in other fields, and have created another machine for cutting cardboard. Tom Zimang has moved on, and now works for the Gallagher group (see Chapter 2), but the partnership they created with him and the University of Waikato is something Ryan considers a huge success, and one they'd like to repeat in the future.

Ryan Manufacturing's high-frequency cheese cutter in action.

7. THE THREE Rs

Rugby, Racing and beeR

Our society is changing. Beer sales are down while the demand for Pinot Noir soars, Lotto has taken over from horse racing as the gambler's choice of dalliance, and let's not even mention the last Rugby World Cup. Having said this, though, there was a time in the not too distant past when our country was firmly based on the three R's of Rugby, Racing and beeR.

And in these three most essential of disciplines Kiwis, predictably, made their mark. We missed the opportunity to invent beer (by about 6000 years), but my word we improved its creation. Given enough time we would have thought up rugby, but the opportunity never arose, so instead we became the best at it, and made the world come up to our standards. Of course, horses were imported into New Zealand, and we didn't invent horse racing but we have had some of the world's greatest horses and we did revolutionise racecourse betting with the automatic tote machine.

Kiwis have come up with any number of games, with more or less success. One game doing well right now is called 'Stonewall'. Invented, perfected and now manufactured in Tauranga by Mark McGregor and the brothers Roger and Grant Bullot in 1996, it is selling in the hundreds a month, and starting to gain attention from overseas. While some New Zealanders are creating better ways to work and produce more for us all, others are busy honing our recreational skills until we are among the world's most prolific and expert lazers-around. This chapter celebrates those men and women. Cheers!

The tote

Odds on he's a Kiwi

Oh, boy. This is a good one! An Australian website loudly proclaims 'Totalisator History: An Australian Achievement', but, in fact, the invention of the automatic totalisator is as much a New Zealand one as it is Australian. It is a story of the birth of the computer, of one of the most lasting social debates in New Zealand history, and of the relentless quest to separate people from their money faster.

Gambling has always been a big part of New Zealand life, and horse racing has long been the most popular way to waste money. When punters place a bet on a horse, the amount of the bet must be recorded. The amount each horse has placed on it is tallied and the odds are calculated by what ratio of bets is placed on each horse. This process is called totalisation. Before 1913, the bets were taken, and these calculations carried out, manually. It was slow and inaccurate, and the race could not begin until all the bets were totalled and the odds calculated. Bookies could run a service (from their spots standing on wooden boxes) just as smoothly. So, despite being legally banned from racecourses in 1911, the bookmakers still pulled in money — probably as much as the racecourse totalisators.

George Julius was born in England, went to high school in Australia, and then came with his family to Christchurch where his father was the Archbishop of New Zealand. He attended Canterbury College in Christchurch and in 1896, with his engineering degree, he moved back to Australia. He worked as an engineer, but in his spare time (as many of us do) he came up with a machine to automatically count electoral votes. This machine was turned down by the Australian government. It was ahead of its time — in fact way ahead, in fact it may never have a time: votes in New Zealand to this day are still lodged and counted manually. Mr Julius (later to be

knighted for his services to technology) converted the idea from one that serves democracy to one that fleeces people out of their money. Despite never betting on horses, he asked a friend to explain the totalisation process to him and then he invented the automatic totalisator.

In 1908 Julius offered his invention to the Ellerslie Racecourse, and in 1913 the Auckland Racing Club held the world's first race meeting where the bets were automatically recorded and computed. It was a huge machine, filling its purpose-made building with what looked like a giant tangle of piano wires, pulleys, sprockets and cast iron boxes, and heavy weights hanging on wires for drive power. It had 30 booths, at any of which a punter could place a bet on any horse. The booths printed a ticket out for each punter

Sir George Julius delivered the totalisator to the world in 1908.

The world's first automatic totalisator, Ellerslie, Auckland.

The first automatic totalisator machine shop.

success. Julius formed a company and had a world monopoly for many years, installing hundreds of his machines all around the world. By 1970, with few exceptions, every major racing centre in the world used these automatic totalisators, which were in service in 29 countries. At first they were purely mechanical, then mechanical and electrical, finally becoming computerised in the 1960s. They also began to put paid to the bookmaker's trade, which finally disappeared after off-course betting was made legal and controlled by the introduction of the Totalisator Agency Board.

Is it fair to call the automatic tote a New Zealand invention? George Julius was not born in New Zealand or Australia, but in England. His degree was from Canterbury and his machine was first installed in Auckland. So despite the fact that the machine was invented and manufactured in Australia, I think we can safely claim it. We'll leave the tote machine with a quote from Sir George Julius himself, talking about the time when he first had the idea to make such a machine. See if you think he sounds Kiwi or Aussie: 'Up to that time I had never seen a racecourse. A friend ... explained to me what was required in an efficient totalisator. I found the problem of great interest as the perfect tote must have a mechanism capable of adding the records from a number of operators all of whom might issue a ticket on the same horse at the same instant.' He's a Kiwi.

and were connected mechanically by wires to the totalisator machine which kept a mechanical tally. The tallies were displayed on the front of the tote building for all to see. When betting was stopped the totals and odds were already calculated. Brilliant! It was effectively a huge computer with 30 terminals and one big display.

Despite a lot of scepticism, it was a huge

Continuous fermentation

The gift that keeps on giving

What Henry Ford did for car manufacturing, our own Morton Coutts did for beer brewing.

For the thousands of years before Morton Coutts was alive, beer was brewed in pretty much the same standard way. The basic method was developed by the Egyptians, who in turn taught the Romans. They, in the process of conquering the rest of Europe, also gave them the gift of beer... and good roads, apparently.

To make beer, barley is soaked in water and allowed to sprout, then the sprouting process is stopped and the result is called 'malt'. This malt is then crushed and mixed with hot water, and the resulting liquid taken away and renamed the 'wort'; hops are added and the whole mess has yeast added to it. The yeast grows and grows until there is five times as much as there was initially. The fermentation process starts, converting sugars into alcohol. This carries on for a few days, and then the beer is aged for weeks or months before being bottled, and shipped to pubs, where you buy it, drink a lot of it and wake up with a sore head.

Morton Coutts fermented
a revolutionary
beer-making process.

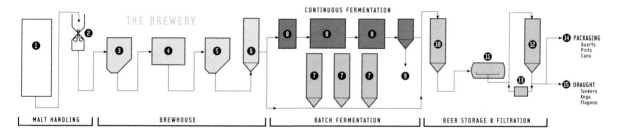

Preliminary Steps ❶ ❷
Malt, hops, sugar and water are the basic raw materials in the brewing process. Malt, held in giant silos (1), is transferred to the malt mill (2) where it is ground before transfer to the mash tun.

Brewhouse ❸ ❹ ❺
The malt is mixed with water to form a mash in the mash tun (3). It is then transferred to the Lauter tun (4) where the malt liquid containing the fermentable malt sugars is separated from the husk to produce wort. This is passed on to the wort boiler (5) where hops and sugar are added and the mixture is boiled.

Wort Stabilisation ❻
The liquor is cooled (6) to freezing point for 48 hours for delivery to batch or continuous fermentation.

Batch Fermentation ❼
This ofers the flexibility for small-volume, speciality brews.

Continuous Fermentation ❽ ❾
NZ's outstanding contribution to brewing technology. The wort is aerated and yeast is added. The yeast takes up oxygen and is thoroughly mixed in the continuous fermentation vessels (8) while the yeast converts sugars to alcohol, CO_2 and flavour. Surplus yeast is later retrieved for yeast extract manufacture (9). Benefits of the process result from the low capital cost, the rapid rate of fermentation and the extremely consistent nature of the product.

Beer Storage/Filter ❿ ⓫ ⓬ ⓭
The fermented liquor is stored (10) and filtered (11) to remove residual yeast proteins. The finished product is stored under refrigeration (12), ready for packing (some beer is recycled to achieve a low alcohol product (13)).

There's nothing wrong with this process, except that it takes a while and in the 1950s and '60s people were drinking more and more beer in New Zealand, and Coutts' employer, Dominion Breweries, was keen to quench their thirst.

Luckily Coutts came at the problem with the ideal family history. Coutts' grandfather was Frederick Joseph Khutze, a man of German heritage who brewed beer for the goldminers in Otago in the 19th century, before moving to Palmerston North to start his own brewery — and why not? The people of Manawatu like a drink as much as the next person. Fred's son, Morton's father, William Joseph Khutze inherited the business of his dad, and promptly shifted it to Taihape, where he correctly surmised that the men working in the timber milling and bush clearing operations in the area could do with some amber nectar at the end of a hard day. William also changed the family name from 'Khutze' to the less-Germanic 'Coutts' — a good move as this was around the time of the First World War. The name 'Khutze' does live on, however, as the name

A good Kiwi head.

of a brand of lager put out by Dominion Breweries in the 1970s and '80s.

William died in 1918 of the flu, and so Morton, aged only 15, took over the business. Talk about a recipe for disaster — would you leave your teenager in charge of a brewery?

But, as it turned out, it was a recipe for something entirely different, for Morton had a brainstorm. If the whole process of growing the yeast and fermenting the alcohol could be separated, the whole brewing process could be made continuous. He began with clearer wort — and isn't that what any of us would want, no one likes the idea of cloudy wort — and worked out a way he could keep shoving yeast in one end and have beer come out the other. Through judicious control of the amount of oxygen given to the yeast at different stages, he could encourage it to either grow or ferment. The brewing process was slashed from 15 weeks to 18 hours.

And luck was on the side of continuous fermentation: DB were refurbishing their breweries at the around the same time, and when they saw the advantages of the system they moved their production to use this technique. Also, perhaps not too coincidentally, the way the government excise of alcohol worked at this time meant there was less tax on continuously fermented beer.

The final stamp of approval came in 1968, when a beer created with this technique won the Commonwealth Beers Championship Cup, a much sought-after prize indeed. The continuous fermentation system that Coutts invented is now commonly used worldwide, and the system is the mainstay of many Kiwi beers.

As an addendum, you may be interested to know that Morton Coutts continued to invent new ways to make beer. In 1993, at the age of 90, he registered another patent, improving on the brewing process again. I guess, at least figuratively speaking, beer is in his blood.

The referee's whistle

When rugby meets dog trialling

Kiwi's didn't invent the whistle, nor, as we've established, did we invent rugby, or even sport in general, but invention is not always about creating something new, it can be about using existing things in new ways.

In 1884, William Harrington Atack was refereeing a game of rugby in Canterbury, New Zealand, using the accepted mode of the time, namely, yelling at the players when they did something wrong. This approach was far from ideal, straining the voice and exhausting the ref. Putting his hand in his pocket he discovered he'd left his dog whistle there, which sparked an idea. The next game he refereed, he sought the players' permission to use one, and the world's first sports game was played 'to the whistle'.

The idea, being so simple yet so clever, was quickly adopted worldwide and soon incorporated into the game's rules — and the rules of almost every team sport played now.

The sound all rugby fans love to hate.

It's a shame Atack hadn't bought shares in a whistle factory.

By all accounts, Atack was a born referee; he was described by his family as 'precise and demanding'. He was born in England, moving to New Zealand at the age of two. He was a sportsman himself, representing Canterbury at cricket and working professionally as a sports journalist. There is a story told of him that once, during a trip to San Francisco, he asked the bellboy of the hotel he was in to post a letter for him. Unsatisfied with the boy's vacillating over the time the post was cleared, and unconvinced the boy could do the job, he decided to take the letter to the post office himself. Several minutes later he returned to the hotel to find it flattened to the ground, one of the many victims of the

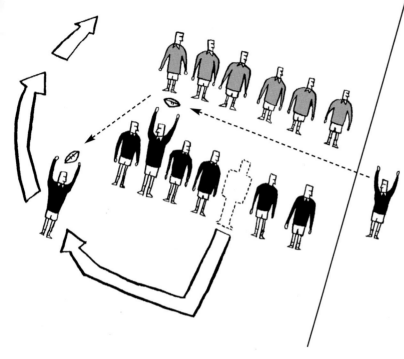

The Willie Away

The ball is thrown into the lineout. A lineout forward taps the ball down to another forward (often a mobile front rower) who races around the back of the lineout and takes play down the middle of the field.

speaking, a Kiwi, but I think it fair to say if he had ever applied for citizenship we would have welcomed him with the open arms of a well-formed scrum.

I think we could state, with no danger of exaggeration, that New Zealanders are obsessed with the sport of rugby. It both galvanises the nation and divides it, depending on whether it's an All Black test or a Super 12 final we're watching this week. Some social commentators have lamented rugby's 'Prozac-like' grip on the nation — a single dose of victory or defeat having the ability to change the mood of the entire nation overnight — but it seems inevitable when rugby is something our tiny nation can excel at on a world scale.

New Zealanders have given hundreds of innovations to the sport of rugby, many intangible (free-running back play), others less so (the haka), but the one with its own name is a move called the 'Willie Away'.

In 1961 the French rugby team were touring New Zealand. The tourists came up against the All Blacks three times in tests during that tour — let me give away the ending here and allay any fears by saying we beat them in every one — but the French certainly gave the New Zealanders a run for their money.

The All Black captain at that time was the great player (now Sir) Wilson Whineray. A front rower (he played at prop for most of his career), Whineray was a born sportsman.

1909 San Francisco earthquake that struck while he was posting his letter.

Atack's 'invention', in hindsight, seems to be obvious — but then, don't many of the best ideas?

The Willie Away

Not as rude as it sounds

In 1850 a schoolboy at Rugby School, in Rugby, England, picked up the soccer ball and ran with it, thus creating an entirely new sport, and an obsession for millions of fans worldwide. This schoolboy wasn't, strictly

As a youth, soccer, swimming and boxing were among the other sports at which he excelled. In fact he ended up winning the New Zealand Universities heavyweight boxing title. Whineray, then a farmer by day, had a rapid rise through the rugby ranks, representing Wairarapa at the tender age of 17, and became an All Black at the age of 21, and named captain a year later. This began a six-year reign which saw Whineray respected as one of the best captains the All Blacks had ever had. He was a tough competitor who expected 'supreme effort' from his team, and he got it.

So imagine his surprise in 1961 at Athletic Park when the French team he was charged with dispatching pulled ahead in the match 6–5, thanks mainly to a strange move off the back of the lineout that set them up for dropped goals. Whineray watched the move with interest, and after the match (which, as mentioned above, they did ultimately win) he set about working on a move of his own using a similar idea.

The move Whineray came up with involves peeling men off from the back of the lineout, who then drive up midfield, creating a blindside. The second five becomes the first five for a switch of play, and the fullback comes up on the newly created blindside. This move effectively commits all the opposition loose forwards and leaves it clear to run the ball around.

The move was very successful, both for

Whineray's rep side, Auckland, where it was employed in the defence of the Ranfurly Shield on more than one occasion, and for the All Blacks, where it became a very effective and prized move.

It was dubbed the 'Willie Away', and Whineray's place in the All Blacks was secured in history. Whineray himself remained in the ABs until 1965, and then set about forging for himself a very distinguished career outside

Wilson 'Willie Away' Whineray – boxer, All Black captain, inventor, company chairman and knight of the realm.

rugby. He went on to become chairman of the Hillary Commission, chairman of Carter Holt Harvey, chairman of the National Bank of New Zealand, a director of numerous companies including the Auckland Airport, Nestle New Zealand and Comalco, and the trustee of many trusts, including the Eden Park Trust and the Halberg Trust. Whineray was knighted in 1998 for his services to sport and business.

Tantrix

Nothing to do with sex

And although we didn't invent rugby, here is a game we did invent — after all, inventing a game is easy. Inventing a game that will last is very, very difficult. A game that is good the first time, good for everyone, and good even for the top 10 players in the world is the game inventor's dream. Can you think of a single game that fulfils these criteria? Chess is hard and frustrating at first and the top players now find that White almost always wins. Trivial Pursuit is easy to pick up, but limited as a competition game by the number of questions that can be invented. Mike McManaway is the inventor of a game and puzzle called Tantrix that he hopes will be as successful as these.

The game comprises 56 hexagonal tiles which have on them different-coloured lines and curves that must be laid, according to the game's rules, against tiles that match up, making continuous lines and loops. The winner makes the longest single-coloured line or the biggest single-coloured loop (loops are worth more points). Tantrix has an element of chance as well as strategy, which means that even a beginner or a child will sometimes beat a champion. This 'luck factor' in Tantrix is just enough for it to be a 'family game'. Over a few games, however, the better player will always prevail — and this makes it great for serious competitors.

When Mike McManaway worked at IBM they taught him that the best way to succeed was to have your own business. Already New Zealand backgammon champion, Mike decided on games as a business and set up a chain of game retail stores. There were over 5000 games in his shops, and with those as his learning ground, Mike began experimenting with game design. In 1988 he had a climbing trip to Patagonia planned. Unfortunately, just before he left, he broke his arm at Whanganui Bay, Lake Taupo. With the tickets already paid for, there was no choice but to go to Chile anyway, where Mike spent his two months' recuperation time designing the game that was to become his life.

The first 2000 games he had handmade in Chile and were sold in his Mind Games shops, but then he began to get the tiles manufactured out of Bakelite — for which he had to go to

The hexagonal tantrix tile.

China. A French houseguest was so impressed by the game that he promised to devote his life to it in return for the European rights, so Mike set him the impossible task of selling a million tiles in the first year as a test. The Frenchman sold one and a half times that to one customer — Air France. That's when Mike sold his shops and went full-time on the game.

Since then Mike has dedicated himself to making Tantrix an internationally popular game. He has not only been the inventor, but the retailer, wholesaler, distributor, player, marketer and evangelist, and he's not interested in inventing anything else. He is not interested in the quick buck, but in putting money back into the game to ensure it flourishes — and it's working. At the time of writing he's sold two million copies of the game over six years, and he's created a popular website (www.tantrix.com) where up to 10,000 games a month are played online.

An important development is the 'Tantrix Discovery' puzzle, which uses just six of the same tiles used in the game. Some of the puzzles take just seconds for a beginner to solve, while others are very difficult, and two of them have never, so far, been solved. The Tantrix Discovery puzzle sets have been responsible for a huge increase in sales. But while they are selling well now, Mike is sure that the lifespan of the puzzle will be short compared to the game — 'Look at the Rubik's cube!'

There is no doubt that Tantrix is easily one of the most successful inventions in this book, not

Mike McManaway demonstrating an undocumented use for Tantrix tiles.

only for the impact it is having on the world, but for the life McManaway has built from it. Commenting on whether or not free play on the Internet might be hurting sales, Mike says, 'Everyone thinks that I ought to feel like that, but I would quite happily go for 20 years without a single cent of income if at the end of that time the whole world was playing it.' Right now there are 56 people trapped at the South Pole from February to October, they have eight games of Tantrix and a dedicated computer server to play it. They are addicted to it.

8. SOD OFF

Locks, oil spills and tin lids

Keeping things out, or in, is the theme of this section. Each of the inventions listed here is created to protect. Maybe it is our island mentality that encourages us to make things that will keep other things away, or maybe it is just the authors of this book trying to come up with a novel way to group inventions. Either way there are a lot of Kiwi inventions that fit into this category.

While researching this book we came across an intriguing reference to a Mr William Bacon, who, it was claimed in a Wellington newspaper in 1961, was the inventor of the Yale lock. Further investigation suggested this was fallacious, and indeed the Yale Company in the United Kingdom were quite indignant about the idea, taking great pains to point out that the Yale lock was invented by Linus Yale in the early 19th century. Whatever Mr Bacon did invent is now lost in the shrouds of time.

Two more that we could confirm, but had no room for, are a device for keeping arsenic out of the water supply in third-world countries (Dr Richard Anstiss at the University of Auckland) and a microwave-based plastic landmine detector (also originating from the University of Auckland).

Woolspill

'Wool you clean that mess up?'

In March 1989, when the *Exxon Valdez* broke up in the waters of Alaska, spilling oil over thousands of square kilometres, the world was shocked and researchers started to look for ways to clean the oil up, other than sopping it up in the feathers of seabirds. It was this tragedy that brought the world's attention to a development of the Wool Research Organisation of New Zealand (WRONZ) for that very purpose.

WRONZ were busy researching ways of manipulating wool for bedding and carpeting. In the 1980s they developed both 'knops' and 'neps' (naps, nups and nips are apparently still under development). Knops are little lumps of wool that are combed out when the wool is carded. Usually rubbish, WRONZ found that when treated and perfumed, these knops make great bedding for duvets and for pillows. These knops are still being used all over the world today. The neps are knops with a furry tail which can be woven into carpet to provide a bit of texture. These too are still being used in carpets internationally.

The knops had further properties. Sheep are greasy-feeling. That is because their wool attracts oils and repels water (hence the saying 'like water off a sheep's back'). About 1990, the WRONZ team thought of using knops made from low-grade untreated wool as oil absorbers. After some research, WRONZ made a major discovery — that wool attracts, and soaks up, significantly more oil when it is rolled into knops. It was a marvellous revelation, and WRONZ were very excited about the prospects for cleaning up the Earth with it. Tested by an environmental science

company in Canada, the wool product was indeed found to be the most efficient natural oil absorber (it was up against stuff like cork, sawdust and straw). There were synthetic products that could suck more oil, but when they were oil-laden they too became waste, whereas the wool had the ability to be cleaned and recycled.

The Gulf War oil spills became a successful testing ground. WRONZ partner Donaghys made special mesh bags to put the wool knops in. When the metres-long bag of wool knops is put onto the spill, the oil is soaked up through the mesh. Water flows through without being soaked up, so the wool 'boom' acts as a filter for the ocean.

The licence to use the technology was sold and the idea was developed into a range of products which are now sold internationally by Orica (formerly ICI). The woolspill booms are still part of the range, but not a big seller due to a lack of suitable oilspills (come on, play the game you oil companies). Bags and pads of wool knops make brilliant filters to remove oil and other hydrocarbons from water that might otherwise enter the stormwater system. These filters are being used in petrol station forecourts, carparks and airports around the world. As worldwide water-cleanliness standards tighten filters like these will become more important. When the knops are woven

into a mat, they can be used under vehicles or leaky machinery. A Dutch railway company uses Woolspill mats to catch oil from its leaky trains. (Although I don't know why they don't just use squashed cardboard boxes like everyone else!)

Securichain

Safe indoors

The typical inventor's stereotype is a guy who finds fault with something he uses every day and comes up with a better way to do it, just for himself. Then, when friends find it useful too,

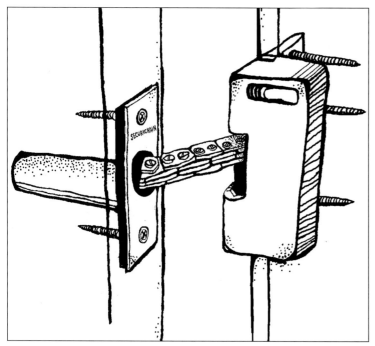

he discovers he can make money from it. This is the story of someone doing it the other way around, in order to develop for himself a money-making business from something that will sell like hot cakes. Obviously, if you really want something that sells like hot cakes, a good tip would be to manufacture hot cakes. They will sell exactly like hot cakes (though whether that is fast or slow is another question).

In 1982 Murray Baber was an agent for various manufacturers' products — a job that he describes as being 'built on sand'. If you do well as an agent, the manufacturer will come and take their business off you, and sell it for themselves. If you do badly, you go under. Murray was looking for a product he could design and manufacture himself that would be saleable worldwide. Being familiar with door-related products, it was natural that he would come up with an idea to improve the familiar security door chain. He reasoned that door security is a worldwide problem, and that if he could significantly improve that product, he might have an impact on the international market. In other words, he might shift some serious units!

But what could possibly be wrong with the common door chain? At first glance, nothing. But that is the inventor's genius, to find some change which would create something that was enough of an improvement to print cash. (Obviously if you really wanted to print cash, you would invent a better cash-printing machine for mints, but that's another story.)

Murray came up with not one, but three problems with the traditional door chain.

1. It is ugly. Maybe it doesn't look bad on your front door, but it certainly sticks out, and is not suited to the décor of a lot of modern apartments or hotel rooms.
2. It is weak. A security measure should provide just that — security. The door chain as we know it is just screwed into the door and the architrave. Any serious force will pull the screws straight out. You may have only seen this happen in films but, yes, it is that easy!
3. It is hard for the elderly or disabled to operate. Putting the knobby-bit into the slotty-bit and sliding it can be a challenge, especially in the dark. Elderly and disabled people, furthermore, are a significant part of the market for security items.

So Murray designed a better door chain. The Securichain is fitted inside the door and the jamb, so that when it is closed the only part that is visible is the little box unit that sits on the edge of the jamb. It looks stylish. The little box has a switch on it. When the switch is one way, the chain will engage as the door opens, preventing the door from opening very far. When the switch is the other way, the chain will not engage, and the door can open as normal. The chain itself sits in the part of the unit which is imbedded in the door and is a miniature version of a bicycle chain, making it very strong.

Murray and his team set themselves the task of making a door chain that could withstand 12 shoulder charges by a 14-stone man (or presumably one shoulder charge each from 12 14-stone men — thus preventing most, but not all, the All Blacks from breaking into your house). They enlisted the help of the DSIR to test the unit and kept refining the prototype until it was strong enough.

The unit is easy to use, as the only thing you have to do is to push the switch, which is very much like a light switch. In order to make the unit stylish, Baber enlisted the aid of Peter Haythornthwaite, an industrial designer. Murray rates this as one of the best decisions he ever made. The product won New Zealand's top design award in 1988, as well as an inventor's award.

Murray's company joined forces with an established company, Interlok, to market the Securichain. They had a spot of bother with

the first version. Securichain Mk 1 had been supplied to a new hotel in Vancouver and when they turned on the air conditioning the Canadian maple doors shrunk. The door no longer aligned with the jamb, and the chains would no longer work. They weren't made to be adjustable, so Murray's team had to design, manufacture and supply the adjustable one.

Since then, all the doors have been open for Murray Baber. Interlock Group Ltd bought out his company and now they manufacture high quality door and window products for New Zealand and all over the world. Securichain is especially popular in new apartments and motels and has been supplied for those in the United States, Canada, Hong Kong, the Middle East, China, Mexico, England and South Africa, among other places.

Murray Baber's success has come not just from a brilliant idea, but from good business sense, great design, strong financial and industrial backing, and sheer good sense.

Sector navigation lights

Providing safe passage for boats

This invention, not for keeping things out but for letting things in, started (as is often the case) with a problem. It was a simple problem, but a deadly one. The entrance to the boat

The Sector Navigation Light was invented as a response to the particularly difficult terrain at Porirua Harbour near Wellington. The exisiting system dictated that two lights were sited one above the other — a configuration impossible at Paremata. Norm Rumsey devised one light source which projected three colours. Steer for the white light and get home dry.

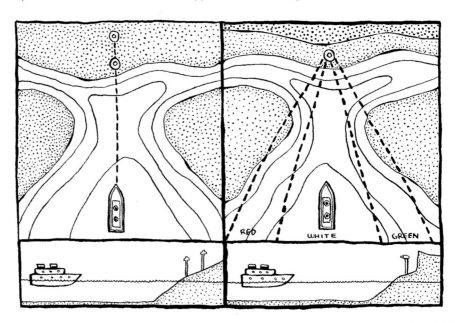

RED   WHITE   GREEN

Red right, green left...
don't forget it!

harbour at Paremata (Porirua Harbour), just north of Wellington, is a difficult passage, with sand bars, rocks and a reef making entry into the harbour difficult and dangerous. Further, the traditional way of marking out the safe entrance to the harbour was unsuitable.

In the past the entrance to boat harbours were highlighted using a system of two lights. One light would be above and quite a bit behind the other light, and the trick for boat captains would be to line the two lights up so they looked in line. If their boats were too far to the left then the top light would look like it was to the left of the bottom light, too far to the right and it would look to the right. When captains could see the two lights atop one another, they would know they were on course.

But in Porirua Harbour, as in many harbours throughout the world, there was a large cliff near the entrance, right where the rear light should go. The separation between the lights wouldn't be sufficient to achieve the effect, so

for many years the Porirua Harbour stood unmarked and treacherous, especially at night.

It was this exact problem that the committee of the local boating club tried to solve when they met one evening in 1961. No immediate solution presented itself that night, but one of the members, Bob Barnes, took the problem to work with him the next day and asked his workmates and, luckily, that was exactly the thing to do, for he worked at the DSIR.

Upon hearing of the problem, Norm Rumsey, an optical physicist, immediately saw the answer. Literally by lunchtime he had a working prototype of the solution, and set in train a tidy solution to the harbour problems worldwide, and a successful local export.

What Norm created was a kind of modified slide projector, with three strips of colour. A narrow white band in the middle, with a strip of red to one side and a strip of green to the other. When approaching the harbour now, captains simply had to make sure they could see the white light. If they saw red, they needed to go right, green, go left — an elegant answer to a perplexing problem.

Of course, the real trick lay in the lenses used to project the light. Normally light breaks up and disperses too much to be of use, but Norm Rumsey's training and background gave him the skills necessary to solve this problem. He had worked for a while designing high-quality lenses to assist in making maps from aerial photos, and could turn his expertise at lens design to the 'sector navigation lights', as they became known.

The DSIR also saw how clever the solution was, and offered the invention for licence to some New Zealand companies. One of them, Vega Industries, took up on the idea and turned it into a million-dollar-a-year business, modifying the original design for other purposes — all of New Zealand's international airports use a 'Rumsey-style' system for the landing lights, with two colours, top and bottom. If they are coming in at the correct angle for landing, the pilot will see two white lights and two red lights; they can use the lights to judge their angle of descent.

But, meanwhile, in Porirua Harbour, Norm Rumsey's lights keep marking out the safe channel, and also serve as a reminder that sometimes the best solutions are the simplest.

Non-chemical weed control

Putting our money where our green mouth is

Weeds are just the plants we don't want. Getting rid of weeds without accidentally getting rid of other living things is a problem we have had since arsenic compounds were first used in the 1940s and then chemical

Steam death to dandelions.

herbicides were introduced in the 1960s. Herbicides are applied to the plants and kill them, but they remain in the ecosystem and damage crops, poison water, poison people, and generally throw a spanner in the works. If New Zealand is to claim to be a 'green' country, we had better come up with a cleaner way to kill the plants we don't want. It is a company called Waipuna International Limited that is finally, on this environmental topic, putting our money where our mouth is.

The seeds of Waipuna International were sown in 1989, when Wellingtonian Graham Collins quit his job as an officer in control of hazardous substances for the Department of Labour. During his 23 years working against toxic chemicals, he became increasingly alarmed at their capacity for environmental damage and decided to do something about it. He teamed up with his mate Richard Newson and they began to experiment with new ways to kill weeds. The resource used had to be natural and have no effect on the rest of the environment, while also being commercially viable. They tried many things — from dog urine, to tree bark extracts, to Student Job Search, and finally hit on...hot water.

The idea wasn't entirely new. People have known for hundreds of years that very hot water kills plants, but nowhere in the world was thermal weed control developed as a viable alternative to chemical weed-killing systems. To do this, they had to find out how much water to deliver, at what heat and at what pressure, for how long — and how to do this economically. After making some working prototypes in 1991, Newson and Collins teamed up with Dennis Tindall, who had been one of the largest chemical weed-killing contractors in New Zealand and was similarly looking for a healthy alternative. (He too had tried many things including flames, steam and liquid nitrogen.) Together they perfected for the marketplace the world's first commercial non-chemical weed-control system. The Waipuna system consists of a truck with a tank of water on it. The water is superheated in the tank, and delivered through a hose to the applicator. The weeds are killed and will not reappear for up to 16 weeks. The results are similar to those gained from chemical spray, but the Waipuna system is ecologically neutral.

By 1995 the Auckland City Council had signed a contract to use the system, and negotiations were in progress to sell the system around the world, but a problem came to light. Almost from day one of testing with city councils, the Waipuna team realised that councils thought the system was too slow — it took too long to apply the hot water. The plants had to be kept heated for a certain amount of time to ensure their weedy little death, and the result is that application costs are higher than for toxic chemical solutions. Of course, in the long run the benefits outweigh these costs but city councils don't necessarily have that vision. So despite having a breakthrough product, Waipuna International went back to the drawing

board. Meanwhile the company was asking investors for patience as they were losing money fast — often millions of dollars a year.

By 1996, the company had come up with a domestic version that kills weeds using only tap water and electricity. It is silent and safe to use. Weeds deteriorate as soon as 24 hours after application, and stay away for up to eight weeks. It is harmless to other plants, the soil, the stormwater runoff, pets and children. As a bonus, it can be used to clean mould, slime and dirt off driveways and houses. At the end of

1999 the first 5000 domestic weedkillers went on the market in Australia and now the domestic weeder is selling so fast there that they can't make enough to supply the New Zealand market. But Waipuna still hadn't satisfied the demands of councils, road boards, rail track maintenance people, landscape gardeners and farmers for a quicker commercial solution. Now, at the start of the 21st century, they have finally completed the research and development needed to solve that problem too. Where hot water weed killing had been thought of before, but never perfected, the new system is a total breakthrough.

When firefighters want to insulate a fire from the air, to smother it, they use foam. Foam is also used as an insulator in buildings. Waipuna International uses a new hot foam method to kill weeds. Instead of holding water on the weeds for a period of time, they have developed an organic foam that, when applied hot, keeps the heat in for long enough to kill the plant for good. The foam is formed from hot water and a special plant glycogen, a sort of plant sugar. When the foam cools down, it is completely non-toxic and has been approved as such by international agricultural organic organisations. Tindall sees the leap in technology from the old hot water method to the new foam method as being analogous with the technological change from 1970s mainframe computers that filled rooms to the powerful laptops of today.

Waipuna International hasn't made its investors rich yet, but it might. The intellectual property for the domestic weedkiller alone has been valued (by an overseas company who value intellectual property for a job) at $100 million, and the foam technology for commercial applications is about to burst onto the marketplace.

Tindall expects the company to bring up to half a billion dollars into New Zealand in the foreseeable future. And that is a whole lot of money where our mouth is.

The airtight tin lid

It's enough to make you cry

Let's cut right to the chase and state that some thieving foreigners stole a great invention from a Kiwi pioneer and left him without a bean. And all because he didn't get a patent....

Consider Milo. No, hang on, let's make it Golden Syrup. Or paint, let's choose paint. In fact all of these things have one thing in common — their lid system. And their usefulness as marital aids, but it's the lid thing we're going to focus on. The lid system on each of these tins is similar, a smaller round plate with a rim that fits snugly into the tin creating a tight fit — airtight, in fact. And this lid system was invented by a Dunedin man, John Eustace.

In 1884 Eustace had a small tinsmithing business in Dunedin, manufacturing, among other things, lids for tins. Back then they were making slip-on lids, which are fine for many purposes, but are sadly lacking when it comes to any application where the contents of the tin need to be protected from the air, such as tins to hold foodstuffs. Eustace and his brother played around with a few ideas, and struck upon the lid system we know today. Pleased with themselves, they started to manufacture the lids, and patented the idea. But here's the rub. They only patented it in New Zealand.

To facilitate the manufacture of the lids, Eustace decided to get a 'die', or cut-out, made in England. The English were obviously very keen to see Eustace's ideas, for not long after his dies were made and returned, the pair noticed that some of the paint they were getting from England had their lid design. They were legally unprotected, and could do nothing to stop a flood of companies in England from basically stealing their idea and making money from it.

To add insult to injury, one London company contacted the pair and offered them the kingly sum of £15,000 to buy the rights to their design, before realising they didn't have to — they could just start making the lids and there was nothing Eustace could do about it. The company retracted their offer, and started manufacturing millions of the lids.

If only Eustace had read our chapter on getting a patent, he could have been a millionaire. It's this kind of experience which certainly fuels the fire of the paranoid inventors nowadays. But, surprisingly, this bad fortune didn't seem to faze Eustace — I suppose he

couldn't let it get to him — he went on manufacturing the lids himself too, enlarging his business remarkably, until, by 1927, he was making 100 tons of tin cans per year.

Yes, this lid is all Kiwi.

9. GREAT CONTROVERSIES

Pavlovas, flying machines and ray guns

We're opening up a huge can of worms with this lot. These are some of the greatest controversies in our country's short history.

New Zealand and Australia share a friendly rivalry over many things: rugby, cricket, CER, GST... but there's one major thing that we compete over that is no joke. This is deadly serious. Come the year 2099, when the War of the Tasman is over and the nuclear cloud over Australasia has dissipated, our great-grandchildren will be wandering around the ashes of New Zealand and Australia thinking: 'All this over a cream-covered meringue cake?' Because if there's one thing that would make us go to war with our trans-Tasman cousins, it's over the right to say 'We invented the pavlova'.

With the desire to finally put this thorny issue to bed, and avoid any unnecessary bloodshed, we examine the evidence, impartially and without bias, and unequivocally state that it was a Kiwi who invented the pav.

The pavlova

Meringue-based gastronomic nirvana

This much is clear and undisputed: in 1926 a Russian ballet dancer, Anna Pavlova, visited Australia and New Zealand. She danced with such grace and lightness as to inspire the inhabitants of both countries, even the cultureless Aussies. Sorry, got a little less than impartial there for a moment, won't happen again.

Another undisputed fact. There exists a cake, made of meringue with a topping of cream and fruit (most properly kiwifruit, but we concede that passionfruit also works) that is also light and graceful. Said cake is popularly known as 'the pavlova'.

And now here's the thing: a) Who invented the cake? b) Who named it 'pavlova'? Read on and be enlightened — be warned, though, that the twists and turns of this ancient mystery may confuse and concern, and at times look bleak and dark, but in the end, we assure you, the side of goodness and right prevails.

In the early 1930s, Herbert (Bert) Sachse was the chef at the Esplanade Hotel in Perth. In 1934 he was asked by the manager to create a new delight for her favoured afternoon teas. He laboured and experimented for a month, and then, as was tradition, he presented the results at a meeting. The cake was a meringue, covered with cream and fruit. It is said that at the meeting the manager remarked 'it is as light as Pavlova' — and so the new cake was dubbed. This story constitutes the core of the Australian claim to the cake.

But don't despair, for not willing to let the matter end on this hearsay and heresy, many New Zealand researchers have worked tirelessly to restore the good name of the Kiwi cooks, and have uncovered two key pieces of evidence.

The librarians of the National Library in Wellington have in their collection a cookery book, published in 1929 — a full five years before the purported cake presentation in Perth — which contains in it a recipe for 'pavlova cakes'. So it may seem that the Kiwi claim is paramount. Not really, because although the ingredients are similar, the recipe describes the process for making three dozen small meringues, not the good old pav as we know it. Damn, our claim looks shaky.

But not for long. In 1927 — now a good eight years earlier than Bert — the good ladies of the Terrace Congregational Church in

ANNA PAVLOVA

GRAND OPERA HOUSE
Wellington
Direction · J. C. WILLIAMSON LTD.
Season Commencing SATURDAY, 12th JUNE.

Price 3d.

Wellington published the second edition of *Terrace Tested Recipes*. In it was a recipe for meringue cake, sent in by a Mrs McRae — blessed be her name — which is exactly the same as the pavlova. Subsequently, similar recipes were published in other magazines in the early 1930s, and then, Bert Sachse himself admitted in a magazine article in 1977 that his creation was really an attempt to improve earlier recipes.

So to all intents and purposes, the inventor of the cake must surely be the mysterious Mrs McRae. But what about the naming of it? In this it looks like the Aussies may have the jump on us. Although they didn't invent the idea of naming cakes per se after Pavlova, it looks like it was they who christened the cake we know today. And it is this that lies at the very heart of the greatest controversy to plague our two great countries.

Now Phar Lap, on the other hand....

Maureen Downs' [my mum] recipe for pavlova

INGREDIENTS

3 egg whites
3 tablespoons cold water
8 ounces sugar
1 dessertspoon cornflour
1 teaspoon vinegar
1 teaspoon vanilla

METHOD

Beat egg whites until stiff then beat in water, and add sugar a little at a time until it's all used. Beat until all the sugar is dissolved. Fold in cornflour, vinegar and vanilla. Line a 20 cm cake tin with baking paper or buttered greaseproof paper. Spoon in the pavlova mixture and bake in oven preheated to 180 degrees Celsius for 15 minutes then turn oven down to 120 degrees for 45 minutes. Remove from oven and cool well away from draughts. Once cool, top with cream and your choice of fruit.

Enjoy!

Richard 'Bamboo Dick' Pearse, the bicycle mechanic whose claim to fame rivals the Wright brothers.

A model of the wondrous flying machine.

Powered human flight

Up, up and a little way

It's so commonplace today that we take it for granted — the ability to jump into an aluminium tube and fly into the sunset. But, of course, for most of human history we've only been able to dream of flying through the air as the birds do. A flying machine has been the subject of many failed inventions, including, most notably, Leonardo da Vinci, who must rate as one of history's best theorisers but worst actualisers. Foreign, he was.

The invention of a flying machine relied firstly on the discovery of suitable scientific principles to base it on. It's all very well watching birds and guessing that wings might be important in flying, but it took Bernoulli's work on aerodynamics and fluid dynamics to get enough science together to use in aircraft design. Indeed, it wasn't until the beginning of the 20th century that serious work could be done on the problem of powered flight. Simultaneously around the world a number of inventors were working on the problem; the ones that concern us are the Wright brothers of America, and one Richard Pearse of New Zealand.

Thanks to their subsequent successes, quite a bit is known about the Wright brothers and their supposedly, and somewhat literally, ground-breaking achievements. They were born in Indiana and Ohio, in the United States, in the late 19th century. They were bicycle mechanics who were fascinated with flying and worked together over a period of years perfecting gliders and playing with engines until finally, on 17 December 1903, they attempted their first (public) powered flight. Wilbur tried first, but in an inauspicious start the engine stalled at take-off. They tossed a coin to see who would try next, an honour which Orville won. At 10.35 a.m. he made a heavier-than-air, machine-powered flight, lasting just 12 seconds and covering a distance of 120 feet — a world first ... or was it?

In contrast, not too much is known about Pearse. He also was born in the late 19th century, and worked for a while as a bicycle mechanic — indeed, Pearse's first patent relates to a new type of bicycle he invented himself. But, like the Wrights, it was flying that was Pearse's passion. In 1902 he built a prototype plane and engine, and then later attempted a powered flight. His too was an

inauspicious start — after a flight of just 50 feet he crash-landed into a gorse bush. The real question is when? When was this attempted flight? No records were kept of the event, but according to circumstantial eyewitness testimony, the date was most likely to be 31 March 1903. That would pre-date the Wrights by eight months!

The controversy really is twofold: whether in fact the attempted flight was before or after the Wright brothers, and whether such a short 'flight' really counts at all anyway. To short circuit the arguments, let's agree that it doesn't really matter. Pearse was a great inventor in his own (w)right, and went on to create a number of interesting inventions, including the aileron, popularly known as the plane's 'flaps'. These are moveable panels in the wing to assist in changing the aerodynamics of the plane, helping to create lift. He also invented, during the Second World War, a plane which could take off and land vertically, presaging the Harrier jump jet and similar planes.

Unfortunately, in his own time Pearse was misunderstood and often maligned. Indeed, he was given nicknames like 'Mad Pearse' and 'Bamboo Dick' (because his name was Richard and he made stuff from bamboo, not a physiological jibe), and died, alone, in a mental institution in 1953. His spirit of inventiveness lives on, and so does his name, being honoured by the Auckland Airport, and on dozens of stamps and streets.

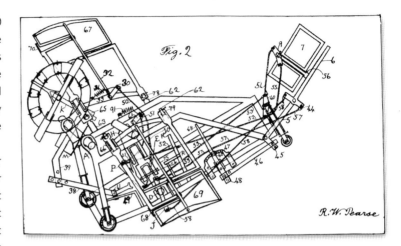

The death ray

Or was it?

It is 1935, between the wars. On Somes Island in Wellington Harbour, the old hospital buildings have been turned into a laboratory where an Auckland inventor called Victor Penny is working on an invention. Day and night, the buildings are guarded by four soldiers with rifles and bayonets. Nobody is allowed to see Mr Penny. If anyone approaches without identifying themselves, they are to be shot. For six months the inventor works at Somes Island, protected from intrusion, and at the expense of the New Zealand government. Word has it he is at work on a weapon called the 'death ray'.

There are really two stories to tell here. The first is the story that the public of New Zealand

The sketch that accompanied Pearce's original patent application.

INVENTION MYSTERY

VICTOR PENNY STILL GUARDED

SECRECY MAINTAINED

MONTHS ON SOMES ISLAND

Nine months ago the "Auckland Star" drew attention to the remarkable fact that a house in Takapuna was being closely guarded by the police. This was the house of Mr. Victor Penny, garage attendant, inventor and experimenter, who on June 19 last was assaulted while on duty at the North Shore Transport Company's garage.

What happened to Mr. Penny? The "Star", after prolonged investigation, is able to say that Mr. Penny has ever since been under Police and military protection while he proceeds with his experiments.

The 'death ray' attracted huge media attention, like this piece from the 'Auckland Star'.

learned at the time from newspaper reports and word of mouth. Because the events were surrounded by secrecy, and because of a lack of understanding of the technology Penny was working on, this story is full of misunderstandings and sensationalism. The second story is the truth behind the events, and will never fully be known. Victor Penny was a very serious man and intensely patriotic. He was sworn to secrecy over the affair, and

took to his grave a good deal of these facts.

The story as the public learned it started in the early months of 1935. A Takapuna garage attendant, Victor Penny (already known for inventing a new kind of microphone), let it be known that he was being hounded by unknown persons, over an invention he was working on. The papers of the day said he was developing what came to be known as a 'death ray'. Rumours and speculation surrounded his work. It was said he had successfully blown up explosives buried beneath the ground, from quite a distance, with an invisible ray that he sometimes had difficulty controlling. But what really got the New Zealand authorities interested was that foreign powers had apparently begun to contact Penny, offering him lucrative contracts to develop his weapon — large sums of foreign money which Penny had rejected. He was supplied with an armed guard and an escort to and from work, but that proved insufficient.

On the night of Wednesday, 19 June, when the armed guard hadn't shown up due to illness, Penny was assaulted at the Takapuna bus depot. His groans of pain brought nearby residents running to find Penny on the ground, his papers strewn around him. 'My papers, my papers, the War Office' was all he could say before he collapsed. The police took extraordinary measures. On 1 July, in great secrecy, Penny was taken by train to Wellington, to Somes Island, to produce the 'death ray' under military protection for New

Zealand and New Zealand only.

It was 19 March 1936 when the veil of secrecy was lifted with the announcement that Penny was no longer in the employ of the government. During Penny's stay at Somes Island, there had been a change of government. The new one was no longer interested in his work due to the fact that there was 'a complete lack of corroborative evidence as to the authenticity of the alleged discoveries'. The implication was that the outgoing government had spent money on a wild goose chase.

And that is as much of the story as ever came out. Penny spoke no more about what he was working on, and the story of the 'death ray' passed into legend.

The truth of this story is somewhat more interesting. What Victor Penny was working on is very likely what we know today as radar. Penny was a self-taught radio engineer, but because of his lack of formal university education, he had a hard time being taken seriously. A gyroscopic compass he invented to hold true north in submarines fell on deaf ears in New Zealand, so Penny sent it off to the Admiralty in London. Some months later a policeman knocked on his door with orders to seize everything to do with the compass. Penny gave it all up except the prototype which, in frustration, he destroyed. He later learned that British submarines were being fitted with a compass similar to his own.

A newspaper reporter present at a seminar given by Penny reported that he was at work on a 'death ray', a headline that infuriated him for its ignorance. Most likely the reporter had become confused about Penny's explanation of radio control, which he was experimenting with.

Radar works by sending out a pulse of radio waves in a particular direction and timing how long it takes for the signal to return, having bounced off an object. The distance to the object is proportional to the measured time. Penny's experiments failed because he could not precisely control the frequency of the radio pulses he was sending; if the frequency is allowed to vary even a little, it won't work. It was technologically impossible to control the frequency of a radio signal using the means Penny had at his disposal — it seems Penny was doomed to failure.

In January 1935 British Air Ministry personnel were considering the possibilities of a 'beam of damaging radiation', while their scientists were advising them to concentrate on using radiation for location rather than destruction. All during 1935 there was a worldwide race to develop and implement radar — a sort of top-secret arms race. In this light it is not surprising that the government, possibly under advisement from the 'mother country', kept Victor Penny under wraps.

Penny returned to Auckland, saying, 'I am not worried at all. I know what I've got and I have not finished my work, not by a long way.' Three years later New Zealand was called to fight in a world war. Luckily for the Germans and the Japanese, we were not armed with Victor Penny's death ray; unluckily for them radar played a decisive role in the Battle of Britain, the sinking of the Bismarck and the American victories in the Pacific.

The wide-toothed shearing comb

New Zealanders beat the Aussies at their own game

New Zealand and Australia both have a strong tradition of shearing that is part of the defining mythology of our two countries. Shearing masters on both sides of the Tasman have been among the greatest heroes of all. New Zealand's Godfrey Bowen broke shearing records all over the world in the 1950s and became an international celebrity — as big a legend as Hillary. In the same decade a controversy brewed that drove a wedge between our two countries in a way that has only been rivalled by the comparatively trivial underarm bowling incident.

It all began in 1898 with the development in Australia of the Wolseley shearing machine. A few years later the machine was good enough to replace hand-shearing in sheds all over both countries. In the beginning both countries used a

Statue at Te Kuiti, shearing capital of the world.

simple 10-tooth comb. Twenty years later and New Zealanders were using a 13-tooth comb from the United Kingdom. It suited our conditions and although it was not taken up by Australian shearers, it was not the comb that caused the controversy. In the early 1950s a new kind of comb was invented in New Zealand. This new invention was a 13-tooth comb, with some of the outside teeth bent slightly outwards. At first only one tooth was bent, now three or four teeth form the convexity, but this slight modification was a breakthrough in shearing efficiency.

Whereas in the early days of shearing, Australians came to New Zealand in droves, adding an 'o' to the end of every word — making 'sheepos' who kept the pens full and 'fleecos' who gathered the shorn wool — now New Zealanders began to go to Australia in search of work. The Australian shearing union was the foundation and the basis of the whole Australian union movement, which was gaining enormous power at this time. The shearing union was very conservative and the presence of New Zealand shearers was a big threat to the solidarity of the workers' movement. New Zealand shearers were willing to work longer hours for less pay, in worse conditions. And, they had a different kind of comb — a better one. With the convex comb Kiwi shearers could shear half as many sheep again in the same amount of time.

The whole Australian shearing rate was based on the old 10-toothed comb. The convex

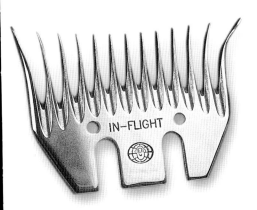

IN-FLIGHT

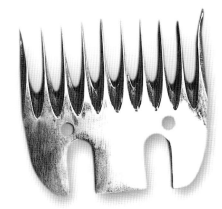

The new Kiwi wide-toothed comb (left) buried its Australian predecessor (right).

comb (called the 'wide-toothed comb' by the Australians) became the scapegoat for all the grievances Aussie shearers had against the New Zealand 'scabs' (or should that be 'scabbos'?). New Zealand shearers' willingness to work harder, combined with their new comb, meant they were an attractive proposition to Australian sheep-station bosses, who hired them to weaken the grip the unions were gaining. The comb was banned by the unions.

When the furore died down, progress was the winner. The convex comb, a genuine product of Kiwi genius, is now the standard comb all over the world and the controversy is all but forgotten. Well, it's at least as forgotten as the underarm bowling incident.

10. CHEATING GRAVITY

Bungy jumping, Fly-by-Wire and the first satellite

For centuries, even before Newton gave it a name, humankind has been seeking a way to break free from the shackles of gravity. As we see in other chapters, Kiwis were among the first to create powered flying machines, and you could say that Hillary's ascent of Everest in 1953 was an attempt to cheat the Earth's gravity by getting closer to the heavens. In this chapter we'll see that our ambition reaches even further than that — out of Earth's atmosphere and into space itself.

Bungy jumping

Near-death plummeting made fun?

I'll come right out and admit that I have never done it and, further, that I am unlikely to ever do it. The idea of hopping out to the end of a wooden platform with my ankles tied together, tethered to the Earth by a long piece of what is essentially elastic, is both frightening and puzzling. Yet people by their hundreds of thousands — granted, many of them foreigners with little command of English and far from the safety of their homes, possibly misconstruing the whole situation and thinking it's some kind of obligatory initiation ceremony or the only way to get a T-shirt in New Zealand — have paid good money to do it.

The idea of jumping off things is not a new one, nor is the idea of stopping oneself

before one gets hurt. Again, like many inventions, it's not necessarily about coming up with a brand new idea, it can be about taking an existing one and making it better. The good people of Vanuatu have for centuries been jumping off large towers, with vines tied around their legs to break their fall. And their legs. This ritual has little meaning for foreigners, and is wholly unattractive, unless billed as some sort of antidote for shortness. What this crazy idea needed was a plan to make it less, well, fatal seeming.

AJ Hackett had just such a plan.

Hackett was a speed skier from New Zealand who heard of the strange Vanuatuan practice, and saw in it the germ of an idea. Hackett and associates developed the 'bungy' — hundreds of strands of latex rubber, bound together into a cord. The bungy was extensively tested until they felt confident it

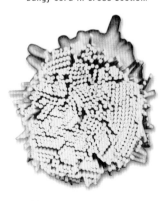

Bungy cord in cross-section.

jumped off into the middle. The deed earned Hackett a lecture from the French gendarmes, but also the respect of thrill-seekers everywhere, and the French themselves. Indeed, at the top of the Eiffel Tower today there is a large memorial to Hackett's feat. 'Memorial' is not exactly the right word, but it has a nice ring of mortality that bungy jumping uses as one of its drawcards.

Over one million people have paid around NZ$80 for the opportunity to 'cheat death', and it should be pointed out that the safety standards of bungy jumping are extremely high. This is thanks in no small part to Hackett and Henry van Asch, who pioneered a set of stringent standards that ensure that bungy jumping is as safe as any other sport where you throw yourself off something solid and into thin air.

would do what they wanted. Hackett undertook his first 'leap of faith' from the Upper Harbour Bridge at Greenhithe, Auckland, and then set about making 'bungy jumping' a worldwide phenomenon.

Hackett's bungy empire now spans the globe, with full-time operations in Australia, France, Canada, the United States and, of course, New Zealand. But I'm still not going to do it.

One of Hackett's strong skills, apart from the apparent disregard for his own life, must be as a showman. In June 1987 Hackett ensured that the legend of the 'crazy Kiwi' would make bungy jumping a financial success by undertaking a bold move. He and a support person snuck up the Eiffel Tower in Paris, slept overnight there, and in the morning attached the bungy to the edge, and

Pickering's satellite

You do have to be a rocket scientist to work here

In the mid to late 1950s, the space race was well and truly on. The USA and the USSR were staring at each other across the Bering Straits and daring each other to outdo their achievements in getting closer and closer to

Explorer I on the launch pad (below).

The Fly-by-Wire adrenalin machine (far right) — check whether it's No. 8 wire when you ride.

the ultimate goal of a person in space.

Imagine the Americans' surprise and envy, then, when on 4 October 1957 the USSR launched Sputnik 1, the first constructed object to orbit the Earth. It did so every 98 minutes, passing over the continental United States seven times a day. Amateur radio fans could tune in to its signals and hear the strange beeping emanating from the unseen object many miles above their heads. It was up there, taunting them.

There was no way the US of A could let that one go, and so in November 1957 they gave the job of creating their own satellite to the Jet Propulsion Laboratory (JPL) of the California Institute of Technology. The JPL was headed by a Kiwi, Dr William Pickering. Pickering was born in Wellington in 1910, but he moved to America to study for his PhD in physics. After a stint as the professor of electrical engineering he helped set up and then run the JPL, which developed, among other things, rockets.

The task before the team at the JPL in 1957 was immense. They were to create a satellite that was technologically the equal of Sputnik, and get it into space as soon as possible. It was a task that they accomplished in three short months. The satellite that they put together was dubbed *Explorer I*, and it weighed a mere 10 kg. It carried with it a cosmic-ray detection package, an internal temperature sensor, three external temperature sensors, a nose-cone temperature sensor, a micrometeorite impact

microphone, and a ring of micrometeorite erosion gauges. Which, I'm sure you'll agree, sounds adequate for the purposes. Crudely speaking, the team at the JPL strapped all this equipment to the top of a rocket, pointed it at the sky and, on 31 January 1958, the USA had caught up.

One of the experiments carried by the *Explorer* was searching for the existence of charged particles high in our atmosphere. The satellite found these particles in a belt, trapped by the Earth's magnetic field, dubbed the 'Van Allen' belt, after Pickering's colleague who had designed the experiment. The discovery of the Van Allen belt by the *Explorer* satellites was considered to be one of the outstanding discoveries of that International Geophysical Year.

The *Explorer I* orbited the Earth every 106 minutes, powered by batteries which helped it transmit its data back to Earth, until they gave out after a mere 31 days, leaving the *Explorer* floating in space as a hunk of useless, but memorable, space junk.

Being a Kiwi, Pickering could be, and was, knighted for his achievement, and he also won many accolades and awards. The JPL, under his leadership until 1976, carried on creating satellites and rockets which helped the United States to explore space — the *Pioneer IV*, the *Mariner* flights to Venus and Mars and the unmanned lunar landings of 1966 and '67 were projects undertaken and led by our top rocket scientist.

Fly-by-Wire

The world's fastest way to spend disposable income

Really successful inventors are often people who have the vision and follow-through to be really successful in many enterprises. Neil Harrap was a successful illustrator, restaurateur, building restorer and antique dealer before he turned his mind to the adventure industry.

Imagine a swing. Now imagine that it is hung from only one rope so that it can swing in big figure eights and in all directions. Now imagine instead of sitting on it, you are lying, facing forward, in a little plane. Now imagine the plane is powered by an engine and you can steer it with a rudder. Imagine all the people, coming to New Zealand to ride this powered swing. This is the very train of imagining that Neil Harrap did in 1994 while lying awake at 4 a.m.

Harrap's Fly-by-Wire plane at Queenstown is suspended from an overhead suspension point, 105 m off the ground, which allows high-speed flight anywhere within the half-hemisphere beneath it. The plane can go up to 170 kph, as high as 100 m in the air, and down to about 3 m from the ground. Maximum 'g' forces are about 3 g — three times gravity — and the pilot has a throttle and steering, so he or she can fly fast or slow in any direction.

The rides in New Zealand have been a huge

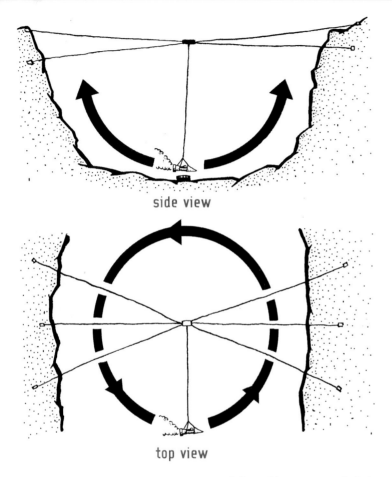

side view

top view

on the suspension wires made the Fly-by-Wire the most complicated tower design problem they had ever encountered.

By the end of the year 2000, there will be up to 20 Fly-by-Wire rides operating in Texas. Fly-by-Wire Ride Parks, each having between three and eight rides, are being set up as we write. Fly-by-Wire are developing the technology of building the rides to the point where they can start cloning rides to install anywhere in the world. Then Harrap will offer the patent rights for sale to companies to set them up in Europe, Australia, Japan and other parts of the world.

Furthermore, Neil is planning to improve the ride, making the planes go sideways while they are going forward (with high-speed sideways translation, like that used in the F-16 fighter plane), using a steerable thruster at each corner instead of just one large thruster at the rear. Other ideas in development are for rides with cable-travel of up to a kilometre in length, and for faster planes — up to 200 or even 300 kph!

What do you need to be like Neil? Well not only an idea, but the vision to see it through to the end. People and management skills, perseverance, savoir-faire, and unfortunately money (or the ability to convince someone to lend it to you). The patenting costs alone, to protect a machine and a trademark like Fly-by-Wire, run to the hundreds of thousands of dollars and to get Fly-by-Wire where it is today, Neil has borrowed millions of dollars.

success, and three rides are currently being built in Texas. Because the land there is flat, each plane is suspended from four 60 m high towers. At the bottom of the plane's trajectory the plane flies into a depression excavated in the Texas earth to create a 'terrain-following' flight effect. The CEO of the American tower construction company said the varying loads

The wobble of Tau Bootis

Science fiction becomes science fact

Astronomers and scientists have always wondered what makes our particular piece of the universe so special. On the face of it, ours is an average star, in an unremarkable part of what looks like a fairly normal galaxy. Why is it that ours has not one but nine planets orbiting it, at least one of which has the capability of sustaining life? What makes us so special?

One scientific theory that can be modified to deal with this conundrum is called 'the anthropic principle'. Simply speaking, it states that things are the way they are because if they weren't we wouldn't be here to see them. So the reason the Earth exists and sustains life is because if it didn't we wouldn't be able to ask the question.

Then there are those who see the anthropic principle as a little trite and useless, and aren't content to let it rest like that. These scientists are searching the universe for solar systems resembling ours — that is to say, for stars with planets orbiting them. Andrew Cameron, originally of Nelson, is one of those scientists.

Cameron went to school at Wanganui's Collegiate College, where he resurrected the school's astronomy club. He completed an honours degree in astrophysics at the University of Canterbury and then left our shores to base himself in Scotland. Cameron is currently a reader in astronomy at the

University of St Andrews, and has been studying our sun, with the hope and expectation that data gathered from it will assist in the understanding of other stars.

In 1996 two astronomers, Michel Mayor and Didier Queloz, detected a regular 'wobble' in a star called Pegasai 51. They deduced it was caused by the gravitational pull of a planet orbiting the star. Gravity works two ways, so when a planet orbits a star, even if that star is very large, the planet 'pulls' the star. The most used analogy, and the most appropriate for this case, is the one of a Scotsman throwing a hammer. As he rotates around and around, holding the hammer at arm's length, he needs to 'wobble' so as not to

Nelsonian Andrew Cameron discovered the millennium planet orbiting Tau Bootis.

be pulled over by the weight of the hammer.

Since 1996, astronomers have used this 'wobble' to detect what they think are 20 other planets orbiting other stars in our galaxy, which is all very exciting, but actually is still just circumstantial evidence. What is needed to directly confirm the existence of other planets is to actually see one. Also, and in Cameron's own words, measuring the wobble 'being an indirect technique...has little to say about the sizes or compositions of the planets, and can only place lower limits on their masses'. In other words, there's only so much you can tell just by looking at the wobble.

Cameron's technique is to look at the light being reflected from the planet, and try to screen it out from the light of the star right next to it. Getting the light coming off a planet is important for two reasons: it shows you that the planet is really there (!), and it can tell you the composition of the atmosphere of the planet. The light absorbed by the planet will be left out of the reflected light, and this will tell you what gases are in the planet's atmosphere.

In December 1999 Cameron did it. He became the first person in the world to 'see' a planet in another solar system. He and his team confirmed with '95 percent confidence' that there exists a planet orbiting the star Tau Bootis, 55 million light years from Earth. They estimate the planet to be approximately eight times the mass of Jupiter, and it orbits its sun every three or so Earth days, at a distance only four or five times the diameter of the planet

itself. This is also remarkable — such an enormous planet so close to a sun, moving so quickly. If we could look at it, it would look like the colour of faded denim, and its temperature would be over 1100°C.

Cameron and his team intend to continue their study of this planet, and others like it, but unfortunately they warn that their techniques won't be able to find the existence of Earth-sized planets in more life-hospitable orbits, so for all intents and purposes, we are still alone in the universe.

The Skystreme kite

Radar reflective fun for the whole family

In 1989, New Zealand adventurer Vernon Pascoe was climbing in the French Alps. I tell you this because it is important to the rest of this story, not because I want to fill you in on Pascoe's holiday habits. Pascoe had been climbing in the mountains many times before with no incidents, but on this particular occasion was very nearly buried alive, when a huge overhanging ledge of snow collapsed on him. This shook him, and made him realise that, had he been buried, the chances of anyone finding him were remote. What Pascoe thought he needed was 'something like a balloon on a stick, to permanently point out where [he] was'.

Over the next eight years, Pascoe set out to create such a marker, although what he came up with was more akin to a kite than a balloon. The 'Skystreme' kite he invented was a tiny (credit card sized) device, weighing only 43 g — about as much as a small bag of chips.

The kite is designed to fly in the slightest of breezes, needing only a wind of 6 kph to get it airborne. The 50 m cord means it flies high enough to be seen for over 3 km from the ground, and it is covered with a metallic coating which makes it reflect radar, and means the Skystreme can double as a thermal vest or emergency first aid splint.

The Skystreme was featured on the BBC world service programme 'Science in Action', and has been tested by the British Royal Air Force and by an expedition to Tibet. And everyone from solo walkers to rescue personnel, and a man who kayaked around

the coast of Britain, are using the Skystreme as a cheap and lightweight emergency beacon.

Gives new meaning to the term 'go fly a kite', doesn't it?

vest

11. HOT DOGS & COLD CHIPS

Sausages, superconductors and the ghost in the machine

In 1999 the New Zealand government expressed their desire to create a 'knowledge-based economy'. Little did they realise that we already have one. We may not be Silicon Valley, with its hundreds of start-up technology companies working towards becoming millionaires with a stockmarket float, but we certainly have at least a small computing and technology industry to be proud of. Indeed it's been estimated that the amount of revenue gained from the export of New Zealand written computer software is greater than that of the wine industry.

There are quite a large number of Kiwi-owned or based companies working away making world-class software for national and international consumption. A couple of these companies have been such spectacular successes as to inspire admiration (and a smidgen, perhaps, of jealousy) from others, whilst making their owners very rich in the process. It seems being from New Zealand, or based in New Zealand, isn't necessarily an impediment in the high-tech world.

Sausage Software

Riding the WWWave of Internet success

It's what every computer geek dreams of — coming up with a cool idea and making millions off it. The 'history' of computing in the last 20 years seems littered with examples of computer geniuses, beavering away in their bedrooms for weeks on end, surviving on nothing but pizza and coke, and then becoming instant millionaires. Kiwi Steve Outtrim is one such geek.

In 1995 — centuries ago in the computer world — Steve Outtrim quit his job to market what he thought was a winning product, a computer accounting package he'd written himself. As part of his attempt to market his package, he decided to utilise the then-fledgling World Wide Web. Steve set about creating some web pages describing his product, and quickly realised that the tools to create these pages were tough to use and very unwieldy, even for a computer programmer like himself. A new idea sparked in his brain, and, ditching the accounting software, he set about writing an easy to use editor for 'HTML' — the language of the web.

In five days Steve had a program he thought worked — 'Hotdog'. Steve then cleverly set about using the World Wide Web itself to help fine-tune his product. He put a message on an Internet newsgroup, asking if anyone would be interested in getting a copy of the program to try out for free. He was flooded with replies — 800 in the first few weeks. Almost unwittingly, Steve had cleverly done two things: he'd enlisted the help of a large number of testers and programmers worldwide to strengthen the product and make it grow but, more subtly, he'd also created interest and demand for his product when it was finished.

Steve launched the first full version of his product in June 1995, three short months after quitting his job. It was an instant success. In the very first week of operation he made over $3000 in sales, in the first month over $36,000, in the first year over $3 million! There wouldn't be many companies in the history of the world with such staggering growth rates. Outtrim was well on his way to becoming a

multi-millionaire from a base of zero capital, and with no real track record. Remember also that Steve was selling his product on the Internet itself, so he had no real overheads, no production costs, and almost no marketing costs. Here is a business model that basically didn't exist even 10 years ago — selling something with no cost of sale.

As an example of the innovative thinking that made Steve's novel approach work, take the time he and a few of his mates decided to go to Comdex, the annual world computer show in Las Vegas. While other companies had been forced to pay hundreds of thousands of dollars for mediocre stands in the main show, Steve avoided this — and also solved the problem that he hadn't booked any accommodation — by hiring a huge mobile home, draping it with advertising for Hotdog, and driving up and down the city streets. The novelty of his idea caught the attention of the media, and Steve also invited senior executives back to his mobile home for a beer, even offering a chauffeuring service, taking them

to business appointments while all the time converting them to the Hotdog way of thinking.

Sausage Software, the Australian-based company Steve went on to form, grew from strength to strength, and is now a huge force in the computer and telecommunications scene over the Tasman. As it grew, of course, Steve was forced to set up more standard business practices — an office, staff and strong management — but the culture of innovation remains.

Postscript: In early 2000 Aussie tele-communications giant Telstra bought 40 percent of Sausage Software, in the process making Outtrim a very wealthy man — to the tune of $163 million.

Superconductors

Better than your average conductors

Conductors, in the scientific sense of the word, are things that transport electricity efficiently. The power wires in your walls are made of copper, which is a particularly good conductor of electricity, not losing too much of the electricity in heat as it passes through. Gold and silver are even better, but for obvious reasons your electrician is reluctant to run gold wires through your new extension.

But even these metals provide 'resistance' to electricity, meaning a little bit of energy is lost as the electricity flows through the wires, making it more costly and less efficient the

more resistance there is. For domestic energy, this 'loss' of energy can be up to 7 or 8 percent from the time it leaves the generator plant to the time it powers your TV. On a global or even a national scale, this amounts to a huge amount of energy 'down the drain'.

'Superconductors' are basically things that don't have this loss, or at least, only lose a very tiny amount of the electricity that passes through them. They promise unparalleled efficiency in powering everything from microchips to power stations to medical scanners. Unfortunately, superconductors only work when it's bollocking cold.

The coldest temperature possible in the universe is minus 273 degrees on the Celsius scale, also known as 0 degrees on the Kelvin scale. At this point matter basically freezes, and all motion of atoms and molecules stops. Not surprisingly, it is beyond our capabilities to create temperatures this cold, but scientists today can get within ten-millionths of a degree of it. When cooled to near this coldest limit, certain metals begin to show some remarkable properties. They start to 'superconduct' — that is, allow electrons to pass through them with no resistance at all.

'Brilliant,' the optimists said, 'within 10 years we'll have 100 percent efficiency, levitating trains and a better world.' That was in 1911, and so far, few of these things have taken off (apart from one prototype of a levitating train in Japan). It turns out that superconductors at these extremely cold

temperatures are very expensive to set up. So for many years the search has been on for superconductors that can work at warmer temperatures — that's warmer relative to 0 degrees Kelvin, still not warm enough for you or me to be running around in our undies.

Then, in 1988, Wellington researcher Dr Jeff Tallon and colleagues at Industrial Research Limited in Wellington made a remarkable discovery. Working with ceramic superconductors, they isolated a new oxide superconductor made from the elements bismuth, copper, calcium and strontium. To put the icing on the cake, their superconductor also worked at the positively balmy temperature of 110 degrees Kelvin, or 'only' minus 163 degrees Celsius.

Tallon's invention led in March 1997 to the creation of the world's first large-scale application of a high-temperature superconductor: a magnet used for carbon dating. It was created by a New Zealand company, Alphatech International, and it's an ion-beam switching magnet for the particle accelerator at the Institute of Geological and Nuclear Sciences. There, I bet you didn't even know we had such technology in the country, let alone a company that creates electromagnets for particle beam transport applications!

The magnet is created by surrounding the superconducting material with liquid nitrogen — at minus 200°C the gas nitrogen is a liquid. The nitrogen both cools and insulates the superconductor, allowing it to do its job. And, unlike other large magnets, if the thing breaks apart no oil or pollutants can leak into the atmosphere, instead the nitrogen 'boils' away as a harmless gas.

More recently Dr Tallon made a further remarkable discovery. In seeking to improve the properties of high-temperature super-conductors he discovered a new mixture of elements that was not only a superconductor but also a magnet — two properties thought to be impossible to create together. Such exotic materials may have applications in data storage, telecommunications and other, as yet unimagined, areas of endeavour.

The superconducting magnet, and the material itself, show that our country already has, at least in part, world-class technology companies.

Electrode's eye view of the Superconductor.

Ghost

Clever technology brings big bucks

Imagine a large American company knocking on your door and offering you a fortune to buy your idea. That's pretty much what happened to Auckland computer programmer Murray Haszard, when software giant Symantec gave him US$27.5 million to buy his product, Ghost. Of course, it wasn't quite that simple, but nothing ever is.

The story starts back in 1982 when Haszard left his job at Kiwi Packaging to pursue an idea he'd had for writing a better version of a compiler — basically a program that lets computer programmers write software. He'd managed to find a way to get a compiler to create code that was 10 times faster than before, working in his spare time for four years, and saving enough from his job to allow him to work on the idea full-time for two years. When it was finished, he took his idea to the manufacturer, who wasn't interested, so Haszard started a company to do it himself. The product became reasonably successful, with Haszard travelling the world to sell it himself. He realised after a while that he couldn't sustain it, and sold his product to a more successful competitor in 1992. He describes this as a bitter pill to swallow; he was in no doubt that he had the better product and

Not a bad for a bit of software (other US$26,499,996 not pictured).

the better customer service, but he couldn't compete with the other company who had superior marketing.

Taking the money from the sale, he retreated to New Zealand and his company pared right back from the 11-odd staff over two continents in the past, to just himself again. Once more it was Murray, by himself and cutting code. The next idea he came up with was for a way to copy files between operating systems — the operating system is the fundamental 'language' of the computer — and he managed to create what he considered was a good product, translating files easily and quickly between DOS, Windows, Unix and OS2. But, once again, he had the best product but inferior marketing. He modified his idea when IBM, who saw what he had done with the OS2 part of his program, suggested he write a disk-cloning system for OS2, their operating system.

Murray spent months working out how to do it, and then proudly flew to the United States to show IBM what he'd created. They were very impressed, but not quick to buy. Murray was on his own again, and he licensed the distribution of his product to an American OS2 reseller.

Then along came Windows 95, and a very pleasant surprise for Haszard. He discovered that, with the changes Microsoft had made to the new operating system, his product would work (with a few minor tweaks) on that platform too! Not only that, but all the pre-existing products from the Windows and DOS world wouldn't! He was in a league of his own.

Immediately he contacted his American reseller, but couldn't convince him to concentrate on the Win95 market. Haszard got the rights back off him for this version, and set about plugging the gap in his skills by hiring a marketing manager, John Crisford. Together they explored options for their new product, and a request from the Manukau City Council saw Haszard reworking his product and making it even more powerful, giving it the name 'Ghost'. Ghost is basically a way to copy entire hard disks quickly and easily, and can save hours of time and effort.

They set up an Internet site to sell Ghost — one of the first to sell programs in this way — and Haszard says it was like magic. The sales took off exponentially, doubling each month until they were getting revenues of about US$2 million per month! The product was being sold via the Internet, and supported and marketed in the United States. There's a lesson in this. Haszard's advice is that it's worthwhile having what he describes as 'a North American façade'; he says in his experience Americans like to buy from America, and so it's worth making the effort to give the impression that's what's happening. Haszard says he never found being a New Zealand-based company to be a problem, but having the American look and feel helped in product sales.

Haszard and Crisford parted company, and

Haszard went on to find a new business partner, Gray Treadwell. The two decided the time was right to sell the company and its product, and hired an American firm to manage the process. Early in 1998 they had a real offer from US software giant Symantec, and in 1999 the sale was finalised. Haszard gave Symantec the rights to his product, Ghost, and in return they gave him a cool US$27.5 million.

So now what? What would you do if you had a whole pile of money and nothing much to do. Well, if you're Murray Haszard you go back to what you love — developing. He's writing a software system for business presentations which should be out soon, and he has also invested in a technology company which is making variable speed propellers for planes.

The Hotcake

'A fat sound that retains the original characteristics'

Paul Crowther is best known in New Zealand as the drummer for rock band Split Enz on their first two albums *Mental Notes* and *Second Thoughts*. Overseas, Paul is now best known as the inventor and manufacturer of legendary rock guitar pedal, the Hotcake.

The Hotcake, like other guitar pedals, is a small box that sits at the feet of the guitarist, and can be switched on and off while the musician is in full swing. It adds an effect to the sound of the guitar and is responsible for the distorted, fuzzy sound (mimicking the sound of an overloaded amplifier, without risking damage to the

Paul Emlyn Crowther is front row right...thinking about inventing a guitar pedal.

amplifier) that has been at the heart of rock and roll forever. The idea is to spend thousands of dollars amplifying the sound of a guitar perfectly and then ruin it. But ruin it just right. The effect produced depends on the electronics inside the box, and the Hotcake is globally renowned for its brilliant sound. In music-speak, most distortion effects provide distortion at the expense of the clean, original character of the guitar. The Hotcake retains the underlying quality of the guitar while providing a nice fat, thick distortion that guitarists go crazy over.

Paul was the electronics whizz of Split Enz. he was on tour in the UK in 1976, when he first came up with the Hotcake circuit idea and he put one in a guitar that Noel Crombie used to clown about with. Noel thought it sounded 'too professional', so Paul knew he was on to something and he built one into a box for their guitarist at the time, Phil Judd. The pedal turned out to be something brand new, and other musicians began to demand one. Paul started making more and more and more, and began distributing them to New Zealand music shops in 1977. Paul managed to get some international bands to try his Hotcake, and more often than not, they would be so amazed with the sound that they would take one back with them. In 1994 an overseas guitar amplifier guru, Ken Fischer, made a mention of it in his magazine column and international mail-order sales began to climb.

The list of the bands that use the Hotcake pedal includes almost any New Zealand act ever

— Split Enz, Dave Dobbyn, the Chills, Crowded House, Chris Knox — and any overseas act worth their rock'n'roll salt too including Beck, The Goo Goo Dolls, Blur, Pavement and Oasis.

Now manufacturing the $240 Hotcake takes most of Paul's time. He has sold literally thousands of them, and word of mouth through the Internet has seen his sales increasing. He has just sent his first order to Finland and a distributor in Japan has sold 1000. Paul is canny — he has realised that if you invent Hotcakes, there's only one way they can sell....

The Hotcake — every guitarist's dream.

12. WONDER WOMEN

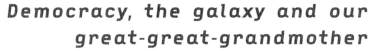

Democracy, the galaxy and our great-great-grandmother

Careful observers will notice in this book an imbalance and an inequality in terms of the representation of the sexes. This is not due to any prejudice or sexism on the authors' behalf, we are sure, rather due to the dearth of female inventors and innovators. That is not to say there aren't any at all – there are just not as many.

We have a theory on this. One reason could be that many inventions are 'motor' or 'mechanically' orientated, and these areas of enterprise traditionally don't interest women. Another reason might be that New Zealand is a very young country, with really only 150 years of inventing history behind us, and for much of this time women weren't afforded the same opportunities in terms of education and training that men had. Shyness or an unwillingness to claim authorship of ideas could be another reason. Yet another contributing factor may be that many inventions (probably 90 percent) turn out to be a useless waste of time, and women are smart enough to avoid this useless effort. Another possibility is that some of the inventions we attribute to males were actually invented by women but, for whatever reason, they weren't given due credit. In fact our very own invention (see Chapter 19) was my wife's idea but she said we could have it!

The origin of the cosmos

New Zealand's own galactic midwife

Beatrice Tinsley (nee Hill) was born in Chester, northern England in 1941, but moved to New Plymouth after the war. She attended New Plymouth Girls' High School, with my mother-in-law who, along with her classmates, called her 'Beetle'. Not in a derogatory way, they claim, but in reference to her name. Her dad was also mayor of New Plymouth for a while, by the way.

Beetle went on to study at Canterbury University, where she decided she would become an astrophysicist — not a decision that comes lightly, I'm sure. After getting their degrees, she and husband Brian moved to Dallas, Texas, to continue their studies. Beatrice gained a PhD with flying colours, getting marks of 99 and 100 percent, and then set about making a name for herself in her chosen area of study, the evolution of galaxies.

On the total scale of things, a galaxy is the biggest known 'thing'. The current model of the universe has it being made up of millions of 'island galaxies', where a galaxy is a collection of millions and millions of stars, some with solar systems like our own (see the work done by Andrew Cameron in 'Cheating Gravity', Chapter 10).

Tinsley's work was on the formation and development of these galaxies and the stars within them. She created models of galactic formation that are said to be more realistic than other models at the time, combining a detailed understanding of stellar evolution with knowledge of the motions of stars and nuclear physics. In short, Tinsley married together many branches of knowledge and created a workable model of galactic creation.

Her work on the origins of galaxies had profound effects on the study of astrophysics at the time, with her work changing the direction of thinking at the time on how galaxies form. Tinsley herself went on to become Professor of Astrophysics at Yale University in 1978, but unfortunately she was diagnosed with

Who would have thought that the queen of the cosmos would be from New Plymouth?

cancer the same year, and passed away three years later, although she continued to work right up until her death.

Throughout her life Tinsley authored over 100 scientific papers, and was heralded as a great scientist, teacher and an inspiration to women scientists both in America and New Zealand.

In 1986 the American Astronomical Society established the Beatrice M Tinsley Prize for outstanding creative contributions to astronomy or astrophysics. The Prize is the only major award in honour of a woman scientist to be created by an American scientific society.

Sheppard adorns our currency and reminds us of her victory.

Democracy

Universal suffrage means votes for all

Sure, you may have learnt in school that the Greeks invented democracy, among other things (mathematics, law and philosophy spring to mind), but it's our contention that democracy in its full sense was in fact invented in 1893 in New Zealand. For it wasn't until this date, anywhere in the world, that men and women could vote equally.

The story of the fight for the vote for women in New Zealand is fascinating from our comparatively liberal position 100 years later.

Many of the arguments and issues surrounding suffrage seem quite silly and blatantly wrong from our privileged vantage point — and I'd have to add that that applies to issues on both sides of the debate.

Let's preface this topic with a bit of background on women's rights. Worldwide, women had, I think it's fair to say, been treated as second-class citizens basically forever. Indeed, the rights of women in most of the western world were, until the mid-1850s, on a par with those of lunatics, prisoners or children. New Zealand, for one reason or another — and in no small part due, I'm sure, to our remoteness from the influence of mother England — was slightly more liberal. In New Zealand, women in the 1800s had a decent chance of getting an education. In fact, Kate Edger, the first woman in the British Empire to complete a tertiary degree, graduated from the University of New Zealand in 1877.

Women were also reasonably well represented in the workforce, employed as doctors, lawyers, and journalists, as well as the 'traditional' teachers and nurses. Yet there still existed the lamentable situation that when the government of the country was being chosen, women's opinions were ignored.

The suffragist movement worldwide had been under way for many years, and it wasn't just women who were asking that their voices be heard. The British philosopher, economist and member of parliament John Stuart Mill presented a petition to the British House of Commons in 1867 calling for the vote for women, but it was ignored, and Mill lost his seat the next year.

In New Zealand the suffragist movement was, for better or worse, entangled with the issue of temperance. Many saw the establishment of voting rights for women as a vote for prohibition, a view that was not helped by the suffragettes themselves, who organised themselves under the banner of the 'Women's Christian Temperance Union' (WCTU). The main concern of the WCTU was that excessive use of alcohol was undermining the family unit and, further, that the woman's work for the economic well-being of the family was being frittered away by Dad drinking all his pay. At the risk of being over-simplistic, the WCTU wanted the vote for women so that women could vote for temperance or, at the extreme, prohibition.

Of course, the idea of giving women the vote wasn't limited to this one issue. The WCTU campaigned for equal divorce laws, raising the age of consent (for sexual intercourse) from the prevailing 12 years, and pre-school education. They were also vocal in their opposition to the

'It does not seem a great thing to be thankful for...'

'It does not seem a great thing to be thankful for, that the gentlemen who confirm the laws which render women liable to taxation and penal servitude have declared us to be "persons".... We are glad and proud to think that even in so conservative a body as the Legislative Council there is a majority of men who are guided by the principles of reason and justice, who desire to see their womenkind treated as reasonable beings, and who have triumphed over prejudice, narrow-mindedness and selfishness.'

Kate Sheppard
on her victory
for human rights

wearing of corsets, which they saw as symbolising the restriction of women.

Katherine Malcolm, more familiar to us today by her foreshortened married name, Kate Sheppard, was one of the leaders of the WCTU and, therefore, of the suffragist movement. Born in England, but moving here as a young woman, she was regarded as highly intelligent and well-educated. She also had a supportive husband, who gave her the encouragement, opportunity and financial means to travel the country expounding her views on women's rights.

Needless to say there were those for whom the idea of women having their say did not hold any joy, and these weren't just the men who enjoyed excesses of alcohol or liked the look of women in corsets. Universal suffrage had one of its biggest opponents in Richard John Seddon, an influential politician whom Kate Sheppard and the WCTU would need to defeat if their cause was to triumph. Between 1887 and 1893 the WCTU presented to Parliament three increasingly large petitions. Indeed, a bill was passed by Parliament in 1891 supporting women's right to vote, but it was subsequently thrown out by the Legislative Council (the upper house).

In 1893 the suffragettes' best chance came. Another bill was passed through the lower house, and it looked like it might head through the Legislative Council also, but then came a blow to the movement. The then Premier, John Ballance, a supporter of women's rights, died, and Richard Seddon became the Premier. He tried to use his influence to change the votes of some members of the Legislative Council, a plan that backfired on him. News of his underhanded approach reached other members of the council, who changed their votes accordingly.

The bill was passed. But it still wasn't law until the Queen's representative and Governor, Lord Glasgow, signed it off. Some efforts were made by opponents of the law to stop him, and in their last symbolic protest, the suffragettes sent camellias to all the members of Parliament — white ones to their supporters, and red ones to their opponents. Lord Glasgow signed, and on 19 September 1893 New Zealand was the first country in the world to have universal suffrage — and real democracy.

The Eve hypothesis

My mum knows your mum

In thinking about how human beings came to inhabit this Earth, there used to be two main schools of thought. There were the creationists, people who took the *Bible*, if not literally, then at least to be substantially true, believing we are all descendants of Adam and Eve. Then there are the evolutionists, those who believe the creation story is a myth, and that all humans evolved from other primates over millions and millions (20, to be exact) of years. The creationists decry the evolutionists and the evolutionists pooh-pooh the creationists. Both ideas seem geometrically opposed: one must be right, and one must be wrong — but which?

Allan Wilson, a biochemist who hails from New Zealand, managed to create a third side to the argument when he claimed it was both. Both were kind of right, and both were sort of wrong.

Wilson was born in Ngaruawahia, educated in Auckland and gained his bachelor degree from the University of Otago. Then, like many of our brightest scientists, he left our shores for America to continue his studies. Ending up at the Berkeley campus of the University of California in the late 1950s must have sparked all sorts of crazy ideas in a young man's head, particularly one with a good working knowledge of biochemistry, and it didn't take long for Wilson to publish his first very controversial theory.

Wilson gained world attention in 1967 when he used a new technique, which he had developed, to claim that humankind was in fact much younger than had previously been thought. As mentioned before, the conventional fossil-dating process had the date of the start of human evolution at about 20 million years ago, but Wilson's technique utilised a comparison of cell DNA from humans and other primates. The fact that such a large amount of the genetic material was so similar led Wilson to deduce that humans had begun their evolution only five million years ago.

As viewers of *Forrest Gump* will attest, the late 1960s at Berkeley was a turbulent, yet creative, period, and by all accounts Wilson was not shy in joining in the demonstrations against the military presence in Vietnam and other protests of the day. In academia too Wilson was seen as a bit of a rebel. Although his theories were backed by as much evidence as any others of the day, he was kept on the fringes of the scientific community, a role he seemed to relish. Slowly he and his ideas became accepted, and he gained prominence in his field.

Then, in the early 1980s, he dropped another bombshell. Wilson claimed he had worked out exactly when, and where, the human race had started. He had created another technique which studied a particular type of DNA found only in females. He and his team studied the diversity of this mDNA from females of many different ethnic backgrounds from all over the world, and concluded that all humans came from one single female, about

200,000 years ago, in northern Africa. So we're all Africans, under the skin.

Well, of course, the results of this announcement were loud and varied. *Time* magazine dubbed it the 'Black Eve Theory'. Academics worldwide criticised it, although they of course had a vested interest in keeping the old theory as that's what they were paid to teach. The media saw it as simple-minded creationism, and even the religious didn't like it that much, although perhaps that was due to the media's simplistic treatment of the theory at the time.

The 'Eve hypothesis' is still a controversial theory, and unfortunately for Wilson he can no longer defend it, as he died at the age of only 55. Today a good deal more is known regarding Wilson's work, and some of the subsequent works have highlighted some flaws in the conclusion, due to errors in the statistical analysis of the work. Even given this, Wilson's work should be viewed as important and ground-breaking, and one of the best steps towards finding our origins in, oh, 200,000 years.

Lucy's agar mission

Seaweed for the war effort

Now I'll bet you haven't given agar a lot of thought. But this unassuming little gelatinous substance is vitally important in many endeavours, not the least in science and meat-canning.

Agar is made from seaweed, boiled down and separated off. The resultant substance is jelly-like and clear, and looks a lot like gelatin, which is extracted from animals. Indeed, you could say agar is vegetarian gelatin, but it is also far superior and is preferred for many things. Agar is used for putting atop canned meat to stop it going bad, it is used in DNA fingerprinting technology, it is used in the soft-centred chocolates Cadbury make, and, perhaps the one we all know from school, it is used in scientific laboratories to grow cultures of bacteria. The little plastic dishes of agar, with its distinctive smell, are the trademark of laboratories the world over.

And in 1941 the sole supplier of agar to the world was Japan. Can you see the problem?

Who could fail to recognise good old Pterocladia lucida?

Of course, Japan's entry into the war meant the agar supply dried up overnight, leaving all sorts of industries in dire straits. The hunt was on for a new source, and fast. And it fell to Kiwi botanist Dr Lucy Moore to provide the solution.

At 35 when the war broke out, Dr Moore, with extensive training in marine botany, and an expert on seaweeds, was the ideal person to find a weed that could not only provide a source of agar but provide it in sufficient quantity to fill all the needs of the nation at war. She was immediately dispatched on a search along the coastlines of the country to find the elusive weed. Her job was simply to find a brand new source of agar.

Moore spent months searching until she found a likely candidate. *Pterocladia lucida* is a seaweed found in abundance around the Bay of Plenty and the east coast of the North Island. Dr Moore found that, when boiled down and separated, the weed proved a source of excellent quality agar — indeed better than the Japanese agar — but now the problem was getting enough of it.

Again, it fell to Moore to solve this issue, and she came up with an ingenious idea. She offered a small amount of money to local schools in return for their students clambering around rocks collecting soggy bits of seaweed. Indeed, when presented with something practical they could do for the war effort, the entire community rallied around and soon seaweed drying on farm fences was a common site right along the east coast.

As it turned out, Dr Moore's work not only assisted New Zealand in times of war, but her discovery of an entirely new source of agar literally on our very shores gave New Zealand another industry that continues even today. One company, Coast Biologicals, processes 200 tonnes of seaweed into agar each year, and with agar fetching about $50 per kilogram on the international market, it's a multi-million-dollar business.

13. HELLO JON, GOT A NEW MOTOR?

Cadac, Smitkin, and the Powerbeat battery

By our, admittedly unscientific and probably quite flawed, investigations, at least half of all inventions seem to relate to engines. Better carburettors, batteries, generators, piston chambers — anything to do with the engine seems to have been the subject of inquiry for an inventor at some time or another. The promise of untold riches for any person who can come up with a better way to propel us through the world seems to be quite real, and — if you'll excuse the pun — a driving factor for many inventors.

Aside from those listed here, there are a number of other noteworthy inventions in this area. In 1966 one Whangarei man invented a rotary engine which he claimed had significant benefits over the Wankel, but since then seems to have faded into oblivion. Industrial Research Limited have created a 'dynamometer', a device which tests the performance of an engine in the workshop whilst simulating 'real-world' conditions, and they seem to have had good success with it. And there are always the stories of people with motors they have invented to run only on water. That these inventions always disappear when investigated could be because they were all bought out by the big oil companies to keep them quiet, or it could be because they never worked. You be the judge.

Godward Economiser

Leaving Invercargill

This is a story about a man who needed to get out of Invercargill. Why he needed to so badly, we will never know, but Ernest Godward, champion athlete, successful painter, musician, politician, public speaker and prodigious father invented something almost 100 years ago that required him to leave Invercargill for London. He was completely successful. Away from his family from 1915 to 1936, he was finally on his way home when he died aboard a ship in Gibraltar.

Godward's first invention got him out of Invercargill and earned him the sum of £20,000, which, when converted to today's money, is almost $1 million. In 1901, he had invented a simple spiral-shaped hairpin which wouldn't slip out of people's hair easily. Taking out an international patent on it, he travelled to the United States for a year, and sold the patent for the above sum. He returned to Invercargill, built a huge house (Rockhaven, which is still standing) and plotted how to get out of the town again, this time for longer.

Among the amazing list of things he did in his life was making motorcycles and bicycles. While working on motorcycles, he began to fit them with a petrol economiser that he had invented. The idea is simple: the more petrol that goes into the engine as a gas or vapour, the more efficient the engine will be. Before fuel can be ignited in the cylinder of an engine,

it must be vaporised. The vapour is what is ignited by the spark, but if the fuel is not well vaporised then globules of fuel will condense and be sucked into the cylinder as liquid and will be wasted. Furthermore, liquid fuel unburnt in the cylinder causes more carbon monoxide pollution than is ideal. The Godward Economiser fits between the carburettor and the engine, taking the mixture from the carburettor and spinning it onto a curved, heated surface. Big drops of unvaporised fuel fall to the bottom where the surface is the hottest, and are vaporised. Smaller drops land at the cooler part of the surface and are also vaporised. The mixture is delivered to the cylinder with no fuel remaining as a liquid, and is thus incredibly efficient.

The genius of the invention is that it was a simple unit that fitted into otherwise normal engines to dramatically increase their performance.

When Godward realised what he had, he saw his opportunity to journey overseas. He went straight to England to capitalise on his innovation. However, he was knocked back by the Poms who couldn't see past the fact that he had no formal education. Even in 1907, it seems you had to have qualifications. So Godward had to come home. He went to university and got his degrees, then in 1914, while the rest of New Zealand's young men were off to fight in the war, Godward was off to America. So it was that the Godward Gas Generator Inc. of New York, and then the

Ernest Godward went to all the trouble of inventing a revolutionary hairpin (below) just to get out of Invercargill.

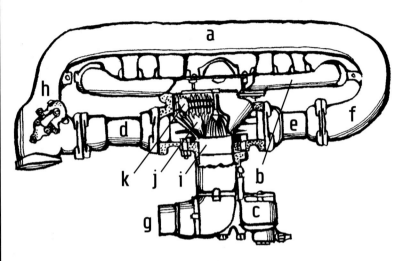

a - exhaust manifold
b - intake manifold
c - carburettor
d - exhaust
e - hot exhaust gas
f - exhaust to gas
    generator
g - air intake
h - winter and summer
    settings
i - raw wet mixture
j - fuel deposited and
    held in suspension
k - 2000 sq. inch heated
    surface

Godward Carburettor Company of London, were formed, and Godward made his fortune.

By 1929, the US Army was fitting Godward's invention to all military vehicles. Eventually Godward Carburettors could be found in cars made by car companies all over the world.

In many ways this is the story of amazing success. It's what is supposed to happen when you invent something worthwhile — as opposed to the story of the Edlin–Stewart engine (see later this chapter), which is a story of financial misadventure, and Nazi nefariousness. Godward's companies must have made him a fairly wealthy man, but more importantly, his inventions have had a lasting effect on the world. However, the pull of the South was too much for him. At 67 years of age, Godward boarded the steamship *Mongolia* to return to his

wife and 10 children. He died before the ship reached New Zealand.

The Smitkin engine

The little engine that couldn't

This is the story of what it really takes, not to invent something brand new, but to improve something that has already been tinkered and tampered with for 122 years.

The engines that are under the bonnets of our cars are fundamentally the same as those first developed in 1876, even before there were cars. In the time since Karl Otto made the first internal combustion engine, only one major departure has powered commercial vehicles in any number, and that is the rotary engine invented by the humorously named German, Felix Wankel. Wankel's major departure was that instead of pistons that moved backwards and forwards in cylinders, there was a three-cornered rotor rotating in a chamber, providing three simultaneous cycles of intake, compression, combustion and exhaust with every turn of the rotor. The rotary engine is very strong on horsepower, but it is not very fuel-efficient.

A new engine will need two major advantages to overcome the difficulty of a worldwide shift to a new technology. No engine so far (including the rotary) has been able to achieve these two aims: it will need to be more fuel-efficient, and it will need to have zero emissions. It will also have to be just as light, just as cheap, just as easy to work on, and so on.

Is an engine like this possible? Absolutely yes, according to the inventor of the 'Smitkin' engine, Roger Smith. But aren't the giant motor companies conducting a covert campaign to quash any new engine with corporate hush money in a worldwide conspiracy to preserve the status quo? Absolutely not, says Mr Smith. He has seen hundreds of new kinds of engines in his years in engine development, and the simple answer is that none of them is good enough — yet.

The Smitkin engine was invented in New Zealand by two Aucklanders, Roger Smith and Graeme Jenkins. After initial testing, it caused a great deal of excitement, both here and overseas. In a press release in March 1997, Graeme Jenkins said, 'It will change the world, provided somebody runs with it. Once one country runs with it, everyone else can't afford not to have it because of its advantages.'

Roger Smith first came up with the idea in the early 1990s. Instead of having a crankshaft, the entire Smitkin engine was designed to spin. The engine shared a lot of the benefits of the Wankel rotary engine but was far more efficient. It was lightweight — a prototype Smitkin made of aluminium weighed around 24 kg, against a similar two-litre combustion engine of 140 kg — and was about the size of a car wheel without the tyre. The diesel Smitkin had 30 parts; a conventional diesel engine has around 3000.

The engine contained no crankshaft, there were no cams, no chains, valves, cogs or bolts inside the engine. It was spark-fired by a CDI ignition system triggered by a hall-effect. The ignition system did not spin with the engine, but the spark jumped directly to the spark plug as it passed a wiper at the desired point for the ignition to occur.

The Smitkin.

It was estimated the engine would be up to 60 percent cheaper to build. Fuel consumption was 40 percent better than conventional engines, it was air-cooled and thus required no radiator, and torque was such that vehicles would require fewer gears. The pistons in the Smitkin engine did not change direction as the engine ran, so there was no running vibration. It was easy to manufacture, and easy to assemble and work on. It showed a 30–40 percent decrease in emissions to exceed all proposed international standards including Europe's planned nitrogen oxide — a feat current auto manufacturers would dearly love to able to match. After initial research showed great promise, a deal was struck with a Chinese firm, the China Sichuan Donghua Machinery Works, to bring the engine to production stage. Basically, it seemed to be the engine that would finally unseat the Otto engine.

But it wasn't. During testing with the

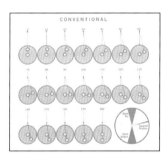

Evidence of the efficiency of the Smitkin engine – apparently.

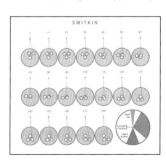

Chinese company, Roger, Graeme and their team had a lot of mechanical trouble with it — they could not stop the overheating. They blew up several engines over the testing period, and eventually the engine was put on hold. The Chinese company is now working with another group on another engine, and Smith is working in secret in New Zealand on an altogether new engine.

Smith and his team of researchers are deadly serious and confident that a new kind of engine is within their grasp. Roger is putting his years of number-crunching research and his experience with the Smitkin towards that new goal. In order to fulfil all the requirements of an engine that will supersede the current one, they are going right back to the beginnings of engine development. The first combustion engines were steam engines — which work on the principle of external combustion (the fuel is burnt outside the cylinder instead of inside it). After the invention of the internal combustion engine, no one has looked back. Roger Smith and his team are looking back. Their new engine will be an efficient, 100 percent emission-free rotary external combustion engine. In Roger's words: 'Watch this space.'

The Edlin–Stewart engine

Steam Stewart and his diesel engine

The story of the Edlin–Stewart diesel engine is a tale of intrigue and deceit, and of intense disappointment. Essentially it is a story of failure. Why the engine failed as a commercial venture is not entirely clear, even today. Maybe the engine just wasn't that good, but certainly the Second World War, the Great Depression, a lot of bad luck, and an element of bad judgement and greed were factors as well. Here it is:

In the early 1920s George Edlin and HH Stewart of Auckland developed a new kind of engine. It was a horizontally-opposed two-stroke engine. Two-stroke engines are inherently efficient as compared to four-stroke engines, simply because it takes only two piston strokes to deliver the power. However, a two-stroke engine has trouble efficiently flushing the exhaust from the chamber in time for the next intake (that's what the other two strokes in the four stroke are for). This means that, especially at low revs, the two-stroke will always run rough. The Edlin–Stewart engine was more accurate and efficient at getting rid of the exhaust and taking in the new mixture. Two pistons shared a common cylinder, and a sleeve inside the cylinder moved in opposition to the pistons. Holes in the moving sleeve formed the valves and both the sleeve and pistons were connected to cranks. Tests at Auckland University throughout the 1920s confirmed the engine's power-to-weight advantages and during tests it was accidentally discovered that the engine (made to run on petrol) was also a very good diesel engine.

Diesel was big news in the Depression

because it was cheaper than petrol. Diesel engines, however, were generally big and heavy and were not used in cars, but only in buses and big trucks. If the Edlin–Stewart engine could be developed as a diesel engine for cars, the sky was the limit — well, the road was. A large public company was formed. Around £60,000 was raised from public subscribers (who might well have been your or my grandparents!) and HH Stewart was sent overseas to show the engine off to American car companies, hoping for a bite.

Despite the Depression having stopped production in car factories all over America, some car companies were still doing research and development, and Stewart impressed the Dodge company with his engine enough that they offered him a deal. They offered the Edlin–Stewart company £10,000 to road test the engines for nine months. During the nine months, the company would not be allowed to sell the engine to anybody else, but if at the end of the nine months the engine was proven worthy, the Dodge company would pay a royalty to the company for each engine that was built. Dodge built a lot of engines, and if the engine was all it was cracked up to be, that deal could have made the shareholders very wealthy. But the company directors turned it down. £10,000 wasn't much to tie up their engine for nine months, they reasoned. So far into the future, it's hard to say for sure but that decision certainly could be the greed and bad-judgement part of the story!

And here is the bad luck part: Word of the engine had got out in the States and famous aircraft manufacturer Howard Hughes was interested in possible applications for diesel aircraft engines. Up until this time diesel engines had been too heavy for aircraft applications. If the Edlin–Stewart engine could power aircraft the sky really would be the limit. Howard Hughes arranged to meet HH Stewart in a New York restaurant. Stewart's taxi driver had other ideas. He took Stewart to New York's dock area where he was robbed and left with nothing. He never did have the meeting with Hughes and the company back home in New Zealand decided Stewart should try and peddle the engine in England.

HH Stewart had a wife and six boys in Auckland, but what followed for him was three and a half years of fruitless struggle in London. England was different than the States. The American dream stipulates that if you are nobody you have still got a shot. There is not even anything called the 'English Dream' and Stewart had a hard time getting anyone to listen to him or look at the engine. Money ran out. Stewart's supporters in London and in Auckland got fed up and wound up the operation. Stewart was left stranded in London, with no way to get home. The engines were lost (probably melted down and fashioned into railings and pokers and

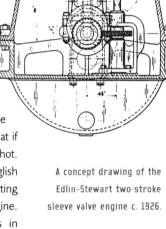

A concept drawing of the Edlin-Stewart two-stroke sleeve valve engine c. 1926.

The
New Zealand Edlin-Stewart
Engine Coy.
Ltd.

REPORT
ON DEVELOPMENTS

Confidential
FOR SHAREHOLDERS

Foreword

It can be claimed for the development of the Edlin-Stewart engine that remarkably satisfactory progress has been made during the short period of two years which have passed since the Company was incorporated in 1930. Experimental petrol and crude oil types of engines have been constructed, additional patents have been secured, and personal investigations and negotiations have been conducted abroad by the Company's representatives. On every hand the principles of the Edlin-Stewart engine have been acclaimed by experts as an outstanding development in internal combustion engines. Realisation of our expectations are now, we confidently believe, within sight, and justification for the confidence of shareholders will be found in the report herein contained.

As the report says: 'On every hand the principles of the Edlin-Stewart engine have been acclaimed by experts as an outstanding development in internal combustion engines.'

Yes, it's the cadac motor generator (top right)!

nutcrackers) and it took Stewart seven months to work his way back to Auckland to his family.

So was the engine ever a real prospect? Well, according to the Stewart family the engine had had a lot of exposure by the time the Second World War broke out, and patents had been lodged internationally. These patents, they say, were stolen and incorporated into the world's first diesel aircraft engine, the Junkers 88, made by the thieving Germans. Stewart still held the patents for the Edlin-Stewart engine and was planning a post-war lawsuit against the Germans when he died in 1951. Just to really add insult to injury, jet engines made diesel aircraft engines unnecessary.

Maybe you're thinking, 'Hey...war, depression, deceit, greed, ingenuity, fate and luck — this all sounds like a great movie!' Well, back off, it's my idea!

The Cadac

A new kind of electric motor

Wellington Drive Technologies are not based in Wellington, but on Auckland's North Shore. They hold a huge amount of intellectual property based around their new kind of electric motors, and they are poised to cash in big time. All going well, according to CEO

Ross Green, the company could nab 1 percent of the world's $US15 billion market by 2003 — possibly sooner. This sounds like an amazing success story, but in fact the company has so far failed to cash in on what is a brilliant technological lead on the rest of the world, a lead they have had since 1987.

The electric motor and generator are everywhere in modern society. Virtually all electricity generated is done so by converting motion (of water or steam) into electricity via a generator, and a good deal of that electricity is converted back into motion via electric motors in homes, factories and in transportation. The basic principles of the electric motor (like that of the car engine) have not changed since their invention in the 1860s by Michael Faraday, so an advantage, if one could be gained, would be a significant revolution in world energy use.

In 1987 New Zealand engineer Peter Clark came up with a great idea for a new sort of electric generator and motor. His vision was a completely iron-free motor. Historically, many of the biggest technological advances in the world have been made with a change of materials. Edison pioneered tungsten to make his new lightbulbs. The semi-conductor technology that revolutionised electronics came with new ways to manipulate silicon. Working in Warkworth, Peter Clark revolutionised the electric motor using newly developed ceramic magnets and thermoplastics. As well as changing the materials, he altered the traditional structure of

the motor. Instead of the coils rotating and the magnet staying put, in Clark's motor the magnets rotated around the current-bearing coil part. The diameter of the spin was increased greatly, which meant the metal content could be further reduced. His work met with early technological success and, by 1995, his lighter, more efficient motors had been put to experimental use in wind turbines, motor-mowers, golf-carts and even solar-powered cars. But financial success was elusive.

The company struggled for the next few years to develop the motor and gain a body of intellectual property. A new CEO with a clear brief to turn technological advantage into profits was brought in and, with Ross Green's help, the company began to focus its marketing efforts. Instead of promising investors motors and generators for all applications, the company turned its focus to small motors, for which the WDT technology is best suited. It just so happens that these small motors (between 1/75th of a horsepower and one horsepower) comprise the largest part of the global electric motor market.

The company has recently made a breakthrough in the electronic circuits that control the motor's performance. WDT's new technology employs radically new electronic control methods with new components and a new way of applying them. If that sounds a bit vague, it's because it is all still quite secret. The

How to fail as an inventor
— Ross Green's Top 10

1. **Make the right product for the wrong time:** your task will be harder when the market isn't ready for your invention.
2. **Pat yourself on the back too much:** New Zealand products have to stack up against those produced in the rest of the world. It's not enough that your widget is better than Joe's down the road.
3. **Think 'No. 8 wire' mentality is cool:** big companies overseas won't be impressed by a little New Zealand company with a widget in a Foodtown bag. We don't have enough street cred for that.
4. **Think ideas equate with reality:** you need a product that works.
5. **Think everyone is interested in you:** don't target everyone. Concentrate on a few areas where you can provide particular advantages.
6. **Make a poor business plan:** it has to be bulletproof before anyone will take you seriously.
7. **Be unsavvy about your competitors:** don't expect your competitors to be too keen to help out developing a product that might make their own product (and expensive plant) redundant.
8. **Spend too early:** don't waste money on plant until you're sure the product is right.
9. **Spend even more too early:** ditto with wasting money on advertising.
10. **Be casual about America:** the US market is more prepared to accept new ideas than most. But fail to deliver, and it'll have you for lunch.

new WDT motors, after more than 10 years of research and evolution, are brushless motors made of plastic, making them smaller and lighter than normal metal motors. They are up to 30 percent cheaper to produce, and run more efficiently, but perhaps the most revolutionary aspect of the motor is that the plastic structure allows the motor to be moulded to 'disappear' into whatever product the motor is part of. The shape-ability of the motor means that no longer will appliances be built around the motor, but the motor can be built to fit the appliance. What shape would a vacuum cleaner or a food-processor be if the shape wasn't determined by the motor? Initially WDT are concentrating on food-processors, air-conditioners and vacuum cleaners as targets for their motors.

Ross Green says an unsuccessful product is 99 percent right. With 13 years of mistakes behind them, with a motor that would be almost unrecognisable to Peter Clark, the originator, and with millions of dollars worth of intellectual property, perhaps the new WDT motors are 100 percent right.

The Powerbeat battery

Power in reserve

The car battery has remained technologically unchanged for many years. Before acid-resistant plastics were invented, the battery was housed in a glass container, but even back then it was basically the same thing. This is certainly not because everyone is satisfied with how conventional car batteries work. Every year, the Automobile Association is called out to approximately 275,000 cars with flat batteries in the Auckland region alone — making the battery by far the most common maintenance nightmare in the modern motor vehicle.

The Powerbeat battery story has made Peter Witehira one of New Zealand's inventor legends. A policeman turned property developer, his life changed in 1987 when he read a book that listed the world's 10 most-needed inventions — including a better car battery. He began cutting up old car batteries and designing a radically new battery. Two years later he founded Powerbeat International on the basis of his design for the Powerbeat DMS (Discharge Management System) battery.

As with a lot of great inventions, the idea is so simple you wonder why you never thought of it. The battery has three parts. First there are the auxiliary cells that store energy for the battery's low-load needs — the radio, the lights, etc. Second the starter cells that store the energy to start the engine. Third an intelligent, electronic system that joins the two sets of cells together when the car is going so it all gets recharged, but disconnects the starter cells when the car is stopped so they cannot be run down. Even if you leave the lights on for days, only the auxiliary cells will be run down. The battery will still be able to start the car, and then recharge itself while running. Further to that Witehira came up with a new double-grid, high-density plate design which allows the battery to stand up to repeated discharge without ill effects — giving it three times the life.

It was a truly revolutionary breakthrough. But to bring an idea like this to market, to unseat the hundreds of millions of batteries in cars all over the world, it has to be perfect. It costs an astonishing amount of money to take a working prototype to the stage where manufacturing can start. Witehira enlisted the help of Dr Evan Bydder of Waikato University to refine his ideas and then set about raising this money, but the next 10 years of the Powerbeat battery story are years of frustration for the company, in terms of funding and manufacturing. Finally, in 1996 a battery manufacturing plant began construction in the Middle East and batteries from there went on the market in New Zealand briefly in 1999, but were withdrawn due to technical difficulties at the plant. Powerbeat says they will be back on the market soon.

Meanwhile, Witehira has built Powerbeat up into the powerhouse of New Zealand invention. Its website lists many inventions under development at its extensive research and development site at Mystery Creek on the outskirts of Hamilton. These include the world's first all extruded-aluminum engine, unique wiper blades with twin blades, and an exhaust scrubber that cleans vehicle exhaust gases of harmful pollutants.

Powerbeat considers about one idea for a new invention each month. With an openness to new ideas and a willingness to stick it out for the long haul and do things properly, Witehira is hoping for a home run, 'We develop a large number of consumer-oriented products and if we hit just one of these home that will be of enormous benefit to this country.'

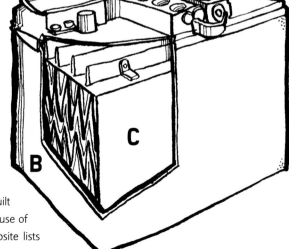

A — **CONTROLLING 'BRAIN'**

The discharge management system (DMS) senses when the vehicle is not in use and isolates the high level starter cells to prevent discharge. The DMS reconnects them when you enter the vehicle and the engine is started.

B — **AUXILIARY CELLS**

These provide the current to power electronics, lights, ignition, wipers, fan, demister and auxiliaries such as the stereo, CB radio and mobile phone. They use special double-grid electrode plates for repeated deep cycling.

C — **STARTER CELLS**

The low density plates are designed to retain full charge to provide the high current needed for quick starting. Connected only to the starter motor they are isolated from other power demands when the vehicle is not running. This way if you leave your lights on you will always have enough energy to start the vehicle.

14. TAKING TRIPS

*The jetboat, Britten motorcycle,
Myark pontoon and
Travelling Buddy*

Kiwis like to travel, upriver, downriver, on the road, on seas and overseas, and, seemingly, we like to invent new ways of doing it. OK, so as far as the rest of the world is concerned we may not have invented the plane (see Chapter 9), and we definitely didn't invent the car, but in 1928 a New Zealand inventor, Charles Crowe of Morrinsville, invented a low-wing monoplane which is said to have been well ahead of its time. This plane went on to assist New Zealand pilots in their pioneering techniques for topdressing.

Alan Croad didn't invent the pushchair, but he did come up with a design for a rugged pram that could go anywhere, which he dubbed a 'Mountain Buggy', and a number of New Zealand inventors (most notably Richard Pearse) have tinkered with bikes and motorbikes for a hundred years, with mixed success. Charles Jones from Mt Cook in 1915 invented a motorised toboggan, a kind of forerunner to the snowmobile, which looked a great deal like a rowing machine, and can still be seen in the Fairlie Museum, in North Canterbury. And, despite a complete lack of any evidence, it's our fervent conviction that the practice of making little model motorbikes out of the tear top lids from beer cans is completely a New Zealand invention. However, if no evidence comes to light, this inventor will have to remain unnamed and unheralded.

Hamilton jetboat

Definitely not invented in Hamilton

CWF (Bill) Hamilton lived at Irishman's Creek in the high country. In 1925, as a wild-haired and mad-eyed 26-year-old, he was the first recorded person in New Zealand or Australia to get in a car and 'do the ton' (100 mph). That alone would be enough to get him in this book. Most blokes would surely have sat back and sighed with a bottle of beer and the cricket on, hand down the pants dreaming of the glory days, but Hamilton kept going. He went to England and raced cars, winning half the time, and bringing back a bride. He designed and made hundreds of implements for moving and shifting dirt and making runways. He made bombs and parts for guns and ammunition during the war. He invented the skifield rope tow. He was crazy about making things. Inventions came out of the workshop at Irishman's Creek like an Australian sprinter — thick and fast.

Finally, when he was 52, Hamilton started to think about something he'd wanted to do since he was a small child — build a better way of travelling up the wild Mackenzie country rivers of his youth. Five years later he was swamped with orders for his invention, the jetboat. Hamilton Jet was born, and is still thriving.

The jetboat is a brilliant way to get around a river. It has high power and requires a draught of only a couple of centimetres of

water, meaning rivers previously navigable only on flounder-back could now be raced up in a big red boat full of screaming German tourists. In the history of boat propulsion, human beings had devised the oar, the sail, the punt, the paddle wheel and the propeller (I'm not counting the Lilo with flippers). It is a fairly major achievement that Hamilton (completely untrained in engineering, draughting, metallurgy, hydrodynamics, or even philosophy for that matter) was able to add the jetboat to that list. Of course, his secret was that he didn't do it by himself.

His first helper was Christchurch boat builder Arnold France. When Hamilton asked France to help him make a boat for shallow waters, France suggested a jet design, and showed Hamilton an American pamphlet on a centrifugal pump design. Bill got his son Jon Hamilton to help him and they made a

If you're doing over 80 kph on the Shotover or Huka Rivers, you have Hamilton to thank....

CWF (Bill) Hamilton, jet boat pioneer.

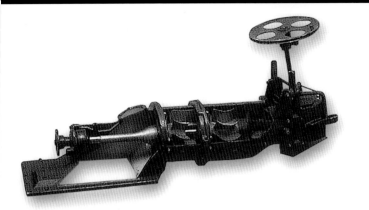

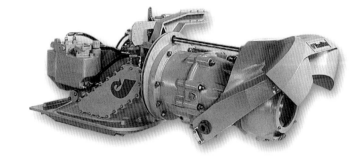

A 1953 Chinook (top) and its more modern equivalent.

centrifugal pump, attaching it to the plywood hull of a 3.5 m boat. It worked, but it was really slow, managing only 17 kph — hardly a break-neck speed. In fact, not even a break-finger speed. After this failure, Bill and Arnold were no longer friends.

Undaunted, Hamilton got his former apprentice, Alf Dick, to help. Dick came up with the idea that the spray from the back end of the jet engine should be ejected above the water, not below it. Imagine a hose spraying out water. The hose can spray water much faster in the air than it can below the water. It

was the same principle that Dick applied to the Hamilton Jet. It worked. The boat now did 27 kph. Good, but not fast enough for the man who had been the first to do the ton.

Next, Hamilton got an engineering graduate from Canterbury University to help. George Davison suggested a new way of approaching the problem — the axial flow. If someone suggested axial flow to you or me, we'd probably just say 'What?', but it was just the trick. Axial flow is basically a tube with a screw or propeller inside it to push the water through. A year later, with the brand new, three-stage axial flow unit on board, Hamilton was cruising at 80 kph! In 1960 a Hamilton Jet successfully navigated the entire Colorado River (up the Grand Canyon), a feat never before accomplished. New Zealand has, since then, been the undoubted world centre of jetboating, and Hamilton Jet still manufactures jetboats and propulsion units for export around the world.

The Myark

'New Zealand is slack – we are leaving'

If you talk to some people, New Zealand is not the inventors' paradise we like to think it is. Denis Stewart is a New Zealand inventor who has succeeded, but against all the odds. He is not afraid to criticise just about every person and organisation on every step in the road that lies between a good idea and a successful product.

Denis had a great idea, and that turned out to be a curse. For six years his unwillingness to give up on his idea turned him into a 'desperate inventor'. For six years, Denis slept in his car (warrant-less and unregistered), with only his dog for company. All the money he could scrape together he needed for payments required for patents to protect his idea. He was winning inventors' competitions all over the country including the prestigious Fieldays Prize, but he couldn't get the help he needed to develop his ideas into a product. In his own words: 'I thought I had a real winner and that everyone would get behind me, family, friends, community council, business development, patent attorneys. They all tripped me up.'

It seemed to Denis as if everyone wanted him to fail. 'How many recent wealthy inventors do you know of, and how many patent attorneys are there in New Zealand?' he asks. 'Something doesn't add up.'

In 1987, sitting on a riverbank, an idea hit Denis 'like a cosmic ray'. The vision was of a folding barge that can be towed behind an ordinary car. The barge is made of aluminium and can be unfolded and launched by one person. The towing vehicle can be driven up onto it for amphibious travel. It is a simple idea, and a product that is not made anywhere else in the world. Deciding to quit his job as a boilermaker and become a travelling hippie, Denis invented the pontoon trailer for himself, so he could take his house-truck anywhere.

The easily transported folding barge.

Because it was a boat on which he could take everything he owned, Denis called it the Myark (My Ark). 'A true inventor is not trying to invent. It happens, it suits his lifestyle, he develops it for himself. Money comes later.' As it turns out, much later.

The invention didn't spring to life fully formed. For six years Denis continued to develop the Myark, patenting it when he could afford to. He tested it on waterways and harbours and even successfully drove it with his car and dog out to Great Barrier, where it sank in a storm. He tried everywhere to get

If your 4WDs can't swim, then Myark is your ark.

support in the form of financial aid or partnership for his invention, but to little avail, which not surprisingly left him feeling the New Zealand system is 'slack' and stifles good ideas.

The breakthrough has come with the idea to hire out the Myark prototypes he has made so far. The film industry is by far his biggest client — using the Myark as a floating camera platform for productions like 'Xena, Warrior Princess'. With this steady income Denis has been able to set up an office, build more prototypes, create a website and get himself to the stage where he is no longer a 'desperate inventor'.

The Myark has turned out to be an incredibly versatile vehicle. It can be used as a barge for salvage, as a diving platform, in the film industry, in tourism for amphibious coach tours, for marine farming, for harbour, lake and river clean-up, for bridge manufacturing, as a portable helicopter pad, for machinery transportation, for ski and jet ski clubs, for flood rescue work, in the armed forces, in entertainment as a stage platform on land and water, for drilling rigs, or as a humble BBQ platform. The hollow pontoons provide space for storage of items both while on the road and on the water. The smallest Myark weighs 450 kg, but will float 3000 kg, and can be towed by even a small car. The biggest is able to float a load of up to 20,000 kg — these are towed by being articulated on the back of a 4WD vehicle.

The Internet has alerted the world to the potential of the Myark and inquiries are coming in from companies and individuals overseas wanting to buy one, or to become business partners. Denis says he and his partner Stephen Snedden are moving overseas to manufacture Myarks. 'I owe New Zealand nothing,' says Denis, 'and I'm going to a country where they respect job opportunities.' Meanwhile Denis is writing a book on his experiences as a wake-up call for patent attorneys, government departments and the typical naïve New Zealander. Denis says he is 'generally gutted' with this country, but when he has made his wealth, he will come back to New Zealand, enter politics and 'kick arse, putting my money where my mouth is'.

The Britten motorcycle

Radical machine from nowhere

Other countries are good at and renowned for quite refined and artistic things — like fine coffee table design, and the world's most elegant china or lace bedspreads. In New Zealand we reject this. We like motorbikes.

In 1994 the name of John Britten joined those of Richard Pearse and Bill Hamilton (whom Britten named as his inspiration) as New Zealand's most famous inventors. Sometimes fame outstrips worth, but in this case his exploits are if anything more incredible than the legend surrounding him. Throwing away the motorcycle manufacture manual and starting completely from scratch in terms of design and materials technology, John Britten and his small team built the fastest four-stroke superbike in the world. On the way they pioneered technology that is now being exploited by motorcycle manufacturers around the world.

At a motorcycle race meeting at Ruapuna in the early 1980s, John Britten and his friends were told they weren't allowed to race their motorcycles in the races for Japanese bikes. They were told to 'F off and start your own club', so they all rode off to Governors Bay and did just that. That was the start of the British, European and American Racing Series, or BEARS. A series was born, and the guys started building V-twin 750 cc motorbikes to race in it. Japanese motorcycles weren't allowed.

Big race clubs everywhere picked up on the BEARS idea and it became a worldwide phenomenon. By 1995 it was a world series with 11 rounds in Europe and America. John Britten had invented the format, and then he went on to invent the motorcycle to dominate it. The Britten bike now smokes all other bikes of its class.

What Britten and his team of engineers came up with in the garage was a revolutionary motorbike, and the racing results are unprecedented. For the fifth year in a row a Britten has won the Sound of Thunder (previously BEARS) at Daytona. Britten bikes have set four world speed records in ordinary race trim, and hold the outright speed record

John Britten developed the motorcycle that became world famous, then world famous in New Zealand.

for Daytona. The world flying mile record (302.82 kph), the world standing quarter-mile (10.759 sec, 134.617 kph), the world standing kilometre (19.33 sec, 186.245 kph), and the world standing mile (27.135 sec, 213.512 kph) were all set in New Zealand by Britten bikes. Britten achieved a long-standing ambition, winning the New Zealand superbike road racing championship series with a bike designed and made in New Zealand.

The praise for Britten's achievement around the world is even louder than we New Zealanders hear: 'It's the world's most advanced motorcycle, and it's not from Japan,

Un-paralleled parallels

Britten designed a girder parallelogram, semi-intelligent front suspension, which is more sophisticated than conventional telescoping forks in that it can tell the difference between a bump and a braking force. The girder system is also significantly lower in weight than a traditional system. Up until the 1950s motorcycles used the parallelogram system but then designs switched to using telescopic forks and the parallelogram was ignored. But the maths says a parallelogram should be better, and John Britten was the first one to try and revisit it. Now there is a race among manufacturers around the world to try and capitalise on the

better maths and make the parallelogram live up to its potential. After 40 years and millions of dollars of investment by motorcycle manufacturers, the telescopic fork system is at the end of its potential.

The patented wheel design uses large diameter axles and a carbon-fibre tubular construction, which makes the wheels much lighter – very important, as they're the unsprung weight on the motorcycle.

The Britten is water-cooled, but in an innovative way. The air is ducted from two nostrils in a high-pressure zone in the shark-nose fairing at the front of the bike to the radiator in a

(Jason McEwen's) Britten V1100.

low-pressure zone under the seat, behind the rider. This ensures a strong airflow for efficient cooling and puts the hot air behind the engine, instead of in front, so that it cools better.

Britten had friends design an engine management system that computer-controls fuel injection and ignition. It was the first time a computer had been used in a motorcycle. V-twin manufacturers all over the world are now taking that idea up. Except for connecting rods (American-made titanium), pistons (British-made Omegas) and gearbox (from a Suzuki GS1100ET), the V-twin engine is entirely Britten's own design and manufacture — casting patterns, castings, matching and assembly. High-tech materials like carbon fibre and titanium are incorporated in the startling pink and blue bike, which weighs a mere 145 kg. The engine produces 170 bhp at 9500 rpm, delivered through the five-speed gearbox.

Britten achieved international praise for his non-traditional methods of construction, and use of carbon fibre. The Britten bike has no frame. The swinging arm (which suspends the back wheel), fork girders, shocks and radiator-subframe all bolt directly on to the engine, which is a stressed member. The wheels, bodywork, swinging arm and fork girders are all made of carbon fibre.

Germany, Italy or America' shouted the cover of American motorcycle magazine *Cycle World*. The cover screamed 'Stunner! — Britten V1100'.

But quite aside from race results and praise, the ultimate compliment is being paid to Britten in the design rooms of bike makers around the world. Britten's design is being copied and adapted to production motorbike manufacture. There is a race on between Triumph and Bimoto to produce the world's first production bike with a carbon-fibre swing arm. Triumph has already copied the ducted cooling system. Computer engine-management systems are now becoming standard on V-twins and axles around the world are now mimicking the tubular construction of the V1000.

John Britten wanted to build just 10 Britten motorbikes. In theory the last one has just sold. Most of the bikes are being raced right now all over the world. Britten's goal was never to manufacture a lot of products. Manufacturing takes the creativity out of design — it demands a tight, anal and disciplined approach to produce an item for a marketable price. John said, 'New Zealand is too far away from most major markets to succeed in mass-production. But I strongly believe there is a niche market for Kiwis to exploit at the high-quality, low volume end of manufacturing. It has to be top shelf.'

John Britten died in 1995, but the Britten workshop is still in full swing today following his vision. Years after he completed it, the

Britten bike is still the fastest motorcycle in the world, which is an incredible achievement.

The Travelling Buddy

Get out on the highway...
with a foam tray

Some of the best inventions seem to arise from someone having a problem themselves, solving it, and then realising that their idea could help others. That's what happened to North Canterbury couple Nicky and Aaron Holder. The Holders have two small children, and they realised what all parents do — travelling in the car with kids is not always an easy ride. Kids drop things, and the attention of the driver can be distracted by having to reach back and pick up dropped biscuits, drink bottles, toys ... it's frustrating for the parents and the children and it's not altogether safe either.

Nicky returned home one day after just such a car ride, and mentioned to husband Aaron, who was a bit of an inventor, that he should invent some way to stop the kids dropping things. Aaron had run a fireworks business until a knee injury saw him leave work and go on the sickness benefit, and he had a bit of time to tinker around with the problem.

What Aaron came up with was a foam tray, moulded to fit in the back seat of a car, and with cut outs for drink bottles, pens, food, toys — anything your average kid might want on a car journey. Aaron's first attempts at the tray saw him burning holes in pieces of foam, but he quickly realised what he was doing was creating toxic fumes, and so set about learning all he could about foam. With virtually no money, no help and no grant to assist, Nicky and Aaron arrived at a solution that they used for themselves, and then started to think how they could make the most of their idea, which they dubbed the 'Travelling Buddy'.

Quick to adapt, the couple expanded their workload, which then featured product development, manufacturing the trays with a press made out of an old supermarket trolley, testing and quality control — not to mention bringing up two children. But they realised they had to get their product out if it was to go anywhere, and so they started the marketing process.

The Travelling Buddy — as popular with parents as with kids.

As many inventors will testify, the idea is only a part of the solution, and a good idea will go to waste if its progenitor sits on their hands — getting people to believe in your product as much as you do, and ultimately pay money for it, that's the real work. When he first started out, Aaron suffered the same self-doubt and nervousness that plagues so many inventors, worried that 'you can't do it, that people are too high up' but, after a while, he came to realise the people at the other end of the phone 'are just like you'.

Nicky and Aaron succeeded in convincing the nationwide chain The Warehouse to stock their product, and are now looking to expand into overseas markets. As well as its use in vehicles, the Travelling Buddy is also suitable for wheelchair-bound people, for those sick in bed, for eating TV dinners and as a versatile tray in numerous other situations. Nicky and Aaron are hoping a little foam tray will go a long way.

The Sealander

It goes on the sea and the land

Terry Roycroft has called his invention the Sealander, because it goes on sea and it goes on land. While that does not seem a very inventive name, the Sealander itself could one day be known as New Zealand's best invention.

Imagine an affordable, mass-produced amphibious car that would drive at motorway speeds on land, then drive straight into the water where it can ride up 'on the plane' (i.e.

Could this be the start of 'lake rage'?

A moment of inventing coincidence

When Terry was tearing around in the Sealander prototype, a friend said to him 'Oh, yeah, Neil's got one like that.' Terry was amazed and went to check out the story. Neil Hyde of nearby Hudson's Bay indeed had a boat that could get up 'on the plane', and could be driven on the land with its three retractable wheels. While Neil's craft was in no way a car, and his objective was different — just to drive his boat from his boatshed to the water without towing — it was amazing that two retractable-wheel planing craft were developed the same year in the same area of the world.

the bulk of the boat sits up out of the water) once it reaches jetboat speeds. It only has to be half as popular as those ridiculous jet-ski things to be a huge success. The reason the world has never seen such a thing is not because people wouldn't want one, but because to make a viable commercial amphibian like this you must solve some very, very difficult engineering design problems. If you have ever sat behind someone towing a boat to Lake Taupo at about 50 kph on the Desert Road then you'll be saying 'Please, please, please be a success!!!'

Like many successful inventors, Terry was, at first, just trying to solve a problem for himself, and make something to impress people with. Living on a farm on the Awhitu Peninsula south of Auckland, the engineering contractor could see the city just a half-hour boat ride away, but to drive there was an hour and a half. In the early 1980s, with time on his hands for a 'major project', Terry decided against agricultural ideas and chose the Sealander. He let the idea brew

in his head and in little sketches for almost 10 years until, in 1991, he was ready to turn it into aluminium reality.

There have been many amphibious vehicles, starting with wartime landing craft, and including a very good VW model based on the Beetle, of which thousands were produced during the war to help the Germans try to fight the Russians. But none of these amphibious vehicles has ever been able to rise up to the plane in the water. What was lacking was a wheel retraction system that not only got the wheels out of the way to allow the craft to go more than about five knots, but would be able to be cheaply mass-produced. When Terry solved that problem, he knew he had something 'pretty damn good'.

The system Terry settled on is based on a normal wishbone suspension that all cars have. It is a cheap and simple solution that disengages the axle and lifts the wheels above the waterline. The car part of the Sealander is mostly Subaru running gear which Terry chose

The Sealander 'on the plane'.

for its good 4WD set-up. The car must be much lighter than a normal car, or it will be a pig in the water, so Terry got the Sealander down to less than half the weight of a normal sedan by use of an all-aluminium monocoque (no chassis or spaceframe) design. The normal car engine (a Subaru 1600 initially, a two-litre now) is disengaged from the wheels and connected to a Hamilton Jet drive unit when the wheels are raised. The steering wheel steers the jet unit when the craft is in the water, where it can achieve a very fast 30 knots. The first prototype, completed in mid-1993, was entirely made in Terry's home workshop at Awhitu.

Now comes the part of the story that is repeated, in different versions, throughout this book. Terry says, 'In my naivety I thought if I could get it going, there would be no trouble attracting capital because it was so unique and exciting.' He filed the patent himself — 'a whole story on its own' — and made some publicity material, attracting attention from New Zealand television and print media, but that was the start of what Terry admits was 'three or four years that were not a good time'.

Finally, Terry hooked up with investor Erny Yeoman and began in earnest to get his working prototype to commercial prototype level. Meanwhile, he learnt a lot about the craft by driving it, and even more by letting his sons drive it. They almost sunk it several times including once with a camera crew on

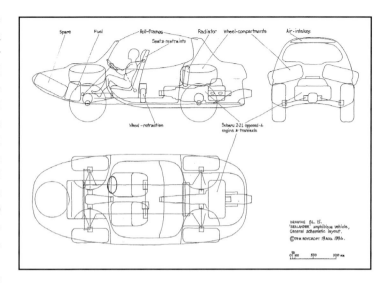

board. Terry kept a four-litre container attached to a long rope on board in case the Sealander ever went down (the first prototype had no airtight compartments and would 'sink like a rock'), so that they could locate it for salvage. Terry's sons have got the knack of hardly even slowing the amphibian down as they approach the water, just timing the wheel retraction perfectly so that it hits the water at 50 kph and just jets right up on the plane. The Roycrofts especially like to pull this move right next to someone struggling to back their trailer down the beach to launch their motorboat.

If you're wondering whether you'll ever be able to buy a Sealander, the answer is yes. The vehicle is currently under development overseas.

A cross-section of a rare hot-blooded amphibian.

15. WAS IT REALLY SUCH A GOOD IDEA?

Jogging, marching girls and the splitting of the atom

Sometimes a nation has to put its hand up and just admit: 'It was me'. Some things you might say the world would have been better off without. Some things weren't a great idea, but someone invented them anyway. New Zealanders have invented a lot of stuff, and not all of it has been what you'd call top shelf.

Some of the inventions in this chapter, then, are inventions that were perfectly suited to their time or place. They must have been, or they wouldn't have been successful enough to go in this book. Still, some of them just don't really seem like a good idea, no matter how you look at it.

Jogging

Queen of the pointless sports

Before jogging became popular, you just didn't see people out in the streets running around. Running was for getting somewhere when you wanted to get there a bit faster than walking and when you didn't have a bike. They reasoned that if you ran out of the house, but then just ran back into the house half an hour later, you hadn't gotten anywhere and there was no point. There was no such thing, then, as a running shoe, and even competitive runners would train maybe half an hour a week. To you and me, this might seem like an ideal situation, this global lack of running around in humorous shorts. But a New Zealander saw fit to change it.

Arthur Lydiard was an Auckland shoemaker, and in 1945 he decided to design a personal programme to keep himself fit. Nine years later he was the New Zealand marathon champion and began to coach young runners using the methods he developed for himself. His basic credo was a combination of aerobic and anaerobic running, as often as two or three times a day for weeks on end, but the combinations were well worked out over years of trial and error. The results speak for themselves. In one hour at the 1960 Olympics, two of Arthur's local athletes, Peter Snell and Murray Halberg, won gold medals; another of his athletes, Barry Magee, got bronze in the marathon two days later. They were just the beginning. Lydiard's programme produced a string of Olympic medals and world records. More than that, Lydiard became a coach of coaches, the world's genuine guru of fitness. It is safe to say that today, no corner of athletics (or fitness training for any sport) is untouched by his influence.

But it's not that influence which concerns us here. When Lydiard came back from the 1960 Olympics as a medal-winning coach, he was asked by his brother-in-law to speak about his training methods at the Tamaki Lions Club. After the talk he was approached by some tubby businessmen who had had coronaries. The wisdom of their GPs said that they should no longer exert themselves. Lydiard said if they wanted to improve their condition they should embark on a programme of training, and he took them out and trained with them. Lydiard began speaking to people all around the country about his Olympic success and how it could be applied to everyday fitness. Flying back to Auckland from Christchurch one day in 1962 with former Auckland mayor Colin Kay, Lydiard told him about his programme. Kay got together a group of about 20 businessmen, few of whom could run 100 m at a stretch. They formed the Auckland Joggers' Club — the world's first. Eight months later eight of them ran marathons.

Ironically, at the time, Lydiard's runners were sponsored by the Rothmans cigarette company. When Arthur was speaking around the country he was working for Rothmans, so he couldn't tell people to stop smoking. 'If I told them to stop smoking and drinking they wouldn't listen to me. I told them to exercise and most of them stopped smoking and drinking a few months later.' He used people's natural competitive instincts in non-competitive training, telling businessmen that, instead of running a circuit around the neighbourhood, they should try running in a straight line and getting their wives to come out in the car and pick them up after an allocated time. The men would run as hard as they could in order to look good.

In the summer of 1963 American track coach Bill Bowerman visited New Zealand with his athletes, as the guest of Lydiard. As well as sharing training techniques, Lydiard one day took Bowerman 'jogging'. The word was new to the American — a 'jog' was what Lydiard called the run you did on an easy day's training. Bowerman found himself lacking in fitness and when he got home to Oregon he set up a local jogging class to get himself in better condition. Bowerman was helping to build a vast and enduring market for his own product, because he was the originator of the waffle-soled shoe that would become the Nike trainer. (Arthur Lydiard will also say, 'I taught Bowerman how to make shoes.'). The running craze took off and spread around America and the planet. The shoe company became Nike, the biggest sports manufacturer in the world. Bowerman wrote the best-selling book *Jogging* and received a

Arthur Lydiard, shoemaker turned instigator of the worldwide jogging phenomenon.

special medal from President Kennedy. His comment: 'I am but the disciple. Arthur Lydiard of New Zealand is the prophet.'

Today Auckland remains the centre of world jogging. The 'Round the Bays' run is the world's largest annual fun run. At the time of writing Lydiard is a remarkably young-looking man in his mid-eighties, still travelling the world to talk about training for fitness. Lydiard's most basic message is that cardio-vascular exercise is good for anyone, no matter what kind of body they have. 'People's bodies are basically all the same. Anaerobic and aerobic exercise affects all people the same way. It doesn't matter how fast or slow they are, the running can give them endurance.'

Rutherford and the split atom

Breaking up is hard to do

In about 400 BC, the Greeks conjectured that the world was made up of tiny particles, invisible to the eye. Different combinations of these particles gave rise to the vastly different materials that we see around us in the world. They called these particles 'atoms' — the Greek word for 'indivisible'. While other variations of this idea of the universe came and went in the following 2000 years, that basic view stuck until about 1850, when scientists discovered that the atom could come with differing electrical charges (positive or negative), and that these charges could change. It was then conjectured that the atom must contain other, smaller particles, but no one had a firm idea on how this all hung together.

Meanwhile, at least for the first 2000-odd years of this, Kiwi Ernest Rutherford wasn't around and so couldn't set them straight. But then he was born, in Nelson in 1871, and the world would never look the same again.

Ernest was, by all accounts, a very clever child, breezing through school, where he seems to have had the quintessential Kiwi education — head boy and in the first XV. He went on to Canterbury College, completing an undergraduate degree and an honours year, and publishing a couple of scientific papers, which got him noticed overseas. He moved to England in 1895 and began as a research student at the distinguished Cavendish Laboratory in Cambridge — the first ever 'foreigner' to be honoured in such a way, and possibly the first example of Kiwis having to leave New Zealand to continue their career.

Rutherford did extremely well in this role, contributing a lot to the work at the laboratory, and gaining an invitation to work at McGill University in Canada, which he took up eagerly. It was at McGill University that he made his first major discovery in science: that atoms can spontaneously 'transmute' into other elements. In layperson's terms, he showed that under certain circumstances some elements can turn into others. It was this work for which he won his Nobel Prize in 1908 — ironically for Rutherford, the prize was for

chemistry, not physics, yet he described himself as a physicist first and foremost.

Returning to England in 1907 he worked first at Manchester University, then back at the Cavendish Laboratory, where he made his next significant breakthrough.

Rutherford devised a plan to derive the internal structure of the atom. It went a bit like this (and by all means, do try this at home...of course you'll need an alpha particle accelerator). Get a piece of gold foil. Beat it as thin as you can make it, almost only a few atoms thick. Now grab your alpha particle generator and point it at the gold foil. (An 'alpha' particle is a large, heavy collection of stuff that should have no problem punching though a little old sheet of gold foil.)

Start firing the alpha particles. Expected result: the particles should smash straight through the foil to the other side. Actual result: they do...mostly. But every now and then one bounces back. Now this was completely unexpected for Rutherford, who likened it to 'firing a cannon ball at a sheet of tissue paper and having it bounce back at you'.

Ernie derived from this result that the atom was mostly just empty space, with something very small and very dense in the middle. Most of the alpha particles pass right through the empty space, but every now and then one of them smacks into the bit in the middle — the 'nucleus' — and is deflected right back. Rutherford had shown that the atom was made up of smaller 'things' arranged like a solar system — small

electrons orbiting a small nucleus. He had, theoretically at least, 'split' the atom.

But not content to finish there, Rutherford went on to actually split the atom; he bombarded nitrogen with alpha particles and witnessed them split into hydrogen. This experiment was Rutherford's third great achievement, and of course seeded the idea of nuclear fission that others would go on to develop into a great boon for humankind, or a great threat to our survival, depending on how you look on it. For Rutherford, it was just good science.

Rutherford's greatest achievement, however, may have been as a teacher and mentor to many of the next generation of eminent scientists — people like Chadwick, Bohr, Oppenheimer and Geiger all learnt their craft from the big Kiwi with the big voice.

Rutherford was at all times an experimentalist.

Rutherford in his lifetime was awarded the Nobel Prize, 21 honorary degrees and countless awards, and was also named 'Baron Rutherford of Nelson'. The story goes that as Rutherford lay on his deathbed in 1937, at age 66, he called for his wife to make a donation of £100 to Nelson College, his alma mater. Today Rutherford's donation is honoured, with his face adorning our $100 note.

Marching girls

It's girls marching

Yes, the sport of marching is a completely New Zealand invention.

If it was the Great Depression and people in New Zealand had no money to spend on leisure activities, could a pastime be invented that would take girls' minds off their troubles, cost nothing and be great fun? Could it be a pastime that would give women a team sport for the summer? Could it be one of the only sports that has ever been invented in New Zealand, to be competed in internationally? The answers are all 'yes', and the sport was marching.

This first record of 'Marching Girls' is in the official history of the visit of the Duke and Duchess of Cornwall and York in 1901. During the Dunedin celebrations, about 500 girls marched past as a celebration of 'girls' drill'. By the late 1920s, marching was established in Otago as a sport. Teams of nine girls were organised and drilled, originally mainly by military men. The marching was based on the *Army Manual of Elementary Drill*, but instead of men calling out orders, the girls took their cues from music. By 1933 business house teams from factories, hospitals and the armed forces were competing in championships and in 1945 a group of businessmen in Wanganui met to form a national body to organise competitions between clubs. Because it was cheap, needed no special equipment or playing fields, the sport developed rapidly.

The 1984 booklet Marching Down Under says 'Is it a sport? Is it an art? Is it recreation? Is it skilful? The answer is Yes, Yes, Yes, Yes... Precision marching, as it is known, has a wide appeal for its colourful, eye-catching, very feminine approach to a sporting activity that borders on the artistic and is a highly skilful, graceful, flowing form of recreation.' And what Christmas parade or telethon would ever be complete without marching girls?

So marching grew as a sport. All over the country young women drilled and drilled, were outfitted in uniforms and competed against rival teams. Teams are judged in competition by deducting points for the most slight and subtle errors: too high an arm swing here, slight misalignment of a head there. Marching associations are grateful to pipe and brass bands for giving them music to compete to, and the bands are grateful to the marchers for giving them a reason to play marches that nobody else really wants to listen to. The biscuit company Aulsebrooks even paid a composer to write the official march of New

Zealand marching. Mr WA Small wrote 'The Aulsebrook March' and it was first performed, recorded and broadcast in 1951.

You might laugh at the idea of thousands of young New Zealand women who keep large hairy hats in their cupboards, but much more stupid sports have become Olympic events. Synchronised swimming, for example, hasn't even got a good name! How much fun would marching sound if it was called 'synchronised walking'? The tall busby-style hats some marchers wear are a recent addition to the uniforms, and by no means mandatory. Throughout the early years of marching in New Zealand they wore more military-style hats, often with a fan of feathers at the front.

It wasn't long before New Zealand marching began to conquer the world. In the early 1950s, several international showcase tours were carried out, resulting in an Australian Girls' Marching Association. By 1977 a competition was held between New Zealand and Australia. This annual Bledisloe Cup of Marching has been contested ever since, except for an eight-year hiatus when the two national associations couldn't agree on the rules for judging!

Perhaps the international highpoint for New Zealand marching is the three times the Lochiel Marching Club of Wellington has been invited to the Edinburgh Military Tattoo. Another highpoint might have served as a warning to the organisers of the sport. In

1993 marching was celebrated on a New Zealand stamp, issued as part of series depicting New Zealand life in the 1940s. If marching had a problem with its image of being something from the past, it began to show in declining numbers of competitors during the 1980s and '90s.

But in 1997 and '98 the organisers did something about it. Working with the Hillary Commission, they started by reorganising the structure and changing their name — from the 'New Zealand Marching Association' to 'Marching New Zealand'. And, as if that wasn't enough, they wrote a mission statement, 'Delivering Marching Opportunities for all New Zealanders'. That's you and me.

NEW ZEALAND

MARCHING
DOWN UNDER

1, 2, 3, 4... you know the rest.

133

16. WANGANUI

The River City spawns its fair share of inventions

What is it about the water in Wanganui? Apart from the fact that it tastes awful and is full of lime, it must also have some positive effect on the creativity and inventiveness of the good citizens of the River City. Our very unscientific comparisons of the inventive outputs of this small town compared with the rest of New Zealand suggests that Wanganui-ites (there's an idea for someone, invent a better name for people from Wanganui) contribute much more per capita to the nation's store of inventions and innovations than citizens of just about any other place in the country. This sleepy hamlet on the bank of the North Island's second longest river has influenced at least one other person in this book, but here we concentrate fully on this celebration of all things Wanganui.

The mighty Whanganui River is not only the second longest in the North Island, with 239 rapids and the site of the historic Jerusalem Maori Mission, but would also make a terrific location for a remake of 'Deliverance'.

The world's fastest machine-gun

A serious weapon not to be taken lightly

During the Second World War, when Jerry and the Poms were fighting it out in France and the Japs were making their imperialistic way down the Pacific, the Allies were in need of a gun that could give them an advantage in the close-range combat that seemed to be the hallmark of the war of the Pacific. Allan

Mitchell, originally of Wanganui but at the time a ballistics engineer for the DSIR, gave them that advantage, inventing a series of machine-guns with ever-increasing firepower.

At the time the Thompson sub-Sten gun had a firing rate of 250–450 rounds per minute. Mitchell created a weapon that was light, easy to disassemble, cheap, and most importantly had a firing rate of over 1000 rounds per minute — that's 16 bullets a second! Mitchell was summoned to a war cabinet meeting to display the weapon, but when he pulled it out he caused a security scare. No wonder, for the weapon he had in his hand could have massacred the entire Cabinet in seconds.

Not content with this amazing weapon, Mitchell created his magnum opus: a machine-gun to be mounted in airplanes that could fire over 6500 rounds per minute — 108 per second! This was four times the speed of the then fastest gun, the Browning, and it remains to this day the fastest single-barrelled machine-gun in the world. Feel free to visit the Wanganui Museum for a close-up look.

It should be pointed out that Allan Mitchell didn't spend his entire life devising more

efficient ways to kill his fellow man; indeed, after the war had finished Allan carried on his grandfather's tradition of diverse inventiveness. Allan Robinson had designed New Zealand's first hydro-electric scheme at Mangamahu near Wanganui, and had also designed all the older bridges in the city — no smirking, these bridges are very pretty.

So it was that Allan (Mitchell) created many innovative devices: a skinning machine for freezing works; an escalator-cleaning machine; not to forget the 'Toaster T bar' — our favourite — a device for stopping toast flying out of the toaster when it's done; and many more.

When not improving machine-guns, Allan Mitchell also invented the 'Goldilocks scourer pot mitt'.

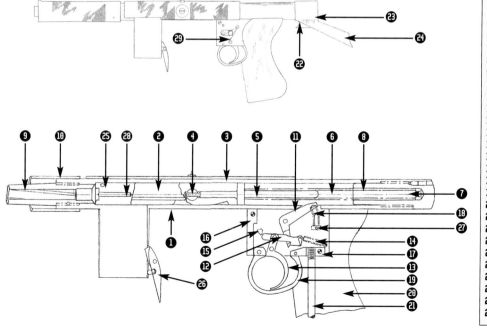

1	body
2	bolt
3	breech cover
4	body pin
5	return spring rod
6	return spring
7	buffer
8	body plug
9	barrel
10	fore end
11	sear
12	trip lever
13	trigger
14	trip lever spring
15	change lever
16	front cover block
17	rear cover block
18	sear spring
19	trigger guard
20	pistol grip
21	pistol grip bolt
22	butt catch
23	butt catch spring
24	butt
25	extractor
26	magazine catch
27	sear spring seat
28	striker
29	assembly spring

In fact, so many more we'd like to keep listing a few of them. Mitchell invented, for the Wanganui City Council, a sort of plough machine for lifting tram tracks out of the main street. He invented a type of fertiliser ('Liquiphos') made out of seaweed. He invented the Goldilocks scourer pot mitt, a mechanical duck plucker and a silent toilet valve.

Mitchell must surely be one of the finest examples of the Kiwi inventor: inventive, wide-ranging in the application of that inventiveness, and with a creation that could wipe out the entire Cabinet in seconds. We need more like him.

Baeyertz tape

Accurately estimating birth dates

You may not know this, but if you go up to a pregnant woman and measure the distance from her pelvic bone to the top of the foetus, you will a) know how far through her pregnancy she is; and b) get a slap. If you do it enough times, and plead that it's for scientific purposes, then you are Dr John Baeyertz, an obstetrician and gynaecologist in Wanganui.

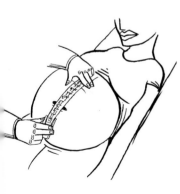

Dr B (as we'll call him, to lessen the chances of misspelling his surname) realised that the traditional methods of calculating a baby's due date — either by calculating from the date of the last menstrual period, or by the date of conception — were both error-prone and unreliable. He had of course heard of the technique of using the measurement from the symphysis to the fundus (doctor speke for 'pubes to the top of the baby'), but likewise there were problems with this technique too. No one had come up with a way to accurately use the measurement, most settled for 'roughly' 1 cm per week of gestation. Compounding this, the invention of ultrasound technology gave hospital doctors very accurate information, leaving GPs out in the cold and on their own.

Dr B realised that with the advent of artificial insemination he could accurately measure the time between conception and delivery, and formulate a precise technique to be used for all women. He spent over 13 years collating the data from 127 pregnancies, including some twins, some abnormal pregnancies, some women who were early, some who were late. From his studies he gained a wide cross section of pregnancy in New Zealand, or, at least, in Wanganui. He could take these results and expect that they would apply to the greater community.

Thanks to his studies, he found that a human pregnancy lasts 266 days with a standard deviation of 4.7 days; that is to say 95 percent of all pregnancies last between 261.3 and 270.7 days — roughly 38 weeks and four days.

This was one of the most accurate measurements of pregnancy ever taken, and gave Dr B the data needed to create a measuring tape calibrated in weeks that could be used by physicians everywhere for predicting birth dates. By 1982, the Baeyertz tape was ready. It is now sold worldwide, bringing Dr B (hopefully) fortune and fame.

The electronic petrol pump

Small New Zealand firm keeps on pumping

OK, so they're strictly speaking not from Wanganui, but from a little township 20 minutes away called Marton, but surely Production Engineering Company Limited have been influenced by the inventiveness of the region.

In 1939 Ray Williams had an idea for a company to make smoke bombs for the war effort. He went and saw his father-in-law, the publican at one of the pubs in Marton, who agreed to loan him the money to start his own business on one condition — that he never leave Marton. And so it was by this kind of blackmail that one of New Zealand's most successful technology companies was based in a tiny farming community in the Rangitikei.

PEC, as they became known, made a variety of products over the years, from armaments during the war years, to ploughs, to electric fences, to mechanical petrol pumps, but in the mid-1970s they began to get an inkling that a big change was on the way. The invention of the microprocessor had a lot of promise, and they could see a day when their mechanical petrol pumps would be a thing of the past, superseded by the electronic age. In true Kiwi spirit they decided not to delay the inevitable, but to jump in head first, and start doing it for themselves.

Indeed, there was another major driver for change. The oil crises of the 1970s were pushing the price of petrol up and up, approaching the $1 mark per litre — and the old dial machines couldn't handle it! They had only been built with two digits. On top of this, the increased cost meant the dials for the cost of the petrol spun faster and faster, and the display on the pumps of the day were jamming more and more often. Something needed to be done.

PEC bought New Zealand's first development kit for the Intel 8080 processor, and the engineers at the company taught themselves how to make the world's first electronic petrol pump — the Empec 80. Their machine got rid of the old Ferranti Packard displays — the flip-over digit ones, like the ones they still have at some airports — and in the process changed the whole dynamic of the petrol station forecourt. No longer did petrol stations need extra staff to assist their patrons with everything; the customers could now preset the amount of fuel they wanted, and new communications systems pioneered by PEC meant the data from the pump could be fed directly into the till. The look of the forecourt changed, and the term 'self-service' took on some real meaning.

PEC bloomed with this new venture. During the 1970s, '80s and into the '90s they led New Zealand and the world in electronic petrol pumps, and in the process grew to employ over 280 staff in Marton — easily the town's biggest employer, rivalling even the nearby psychiatric institution. Of course, they've diversified into other areas too (PEC, not the hospital), most relating to the petrol pump system, but demand for their original products is still strong.

At the time of writing, PEC have just been bought by the Gallagher group of companies (see Chapter 2), and parts of the company split up, although they will continue to produce and innovate. In Marton, however, they are now only a shadow of what they once were.

Childproof lids

Keeps little fingers out of your stuff

You know the ones — the caps on medicine bottles that are ostensibly 'child-proof', but in my experience have foxed unsuspecting adults too. They are the plastic caps you have to push down, then twist in order to open them. They've sold in their tens of millions worldwide, and they were invented in Wanganui.

Claudio Petronelli is an Italian expat who moved to Wanganui and had a family. In 1970 he had a baby son, Antony, and another on the way. Reading the newspaper one day he came upon the story of an unfortunate family in Hawke's Bay whose toddler had found the family medicine cabinet and swallowed an apothecary of drugs, with fatal effect. As a father, Claudio could empathise with the family, and was determined the same would not happen to him. He set about inventing a childproof lid system.

Claudio was an engineer by birth; his father was a civil engineer in Rome, and we all know the reputation of Roman civil engineers — roads were, after all, their specialty! Claudio made a prototype cap in metal, coming up with the 'double-lock' system that we know today. With partner Gavin Park he refined the prototype until he had a working model which they began manufacturing in plastic. They registered their patent, a process they describe as very costly, and set about licensing their idea.

The patent to their design has now expired, but whilst they had it they licensed the manufacture of their childproof lids to an American company, who manufactured millions of them. But Claudio, unlike his Roman ancestors, didn't rest on his laurels. He formed Petronelli Valve Limited, a manufacturing and design company based in Wanganui. The company has created a number of other inventions, from garden tools (the trowel fork is one of theirs), to kitchen utensils (an improved garlic mincer), to water valves, to their latest innovation — an improved manifold, which will be on the market by the time you read this.

Claudio doesn't believe that being based in a small town, or even in a small country like New Zealand, is in any way a disadvantage to the inventor, but he does caution that inventing can be an expensive business — from the initial idea, through prototyping, manufacture, patent applications, legal costs and the like to seeing an income from your idea can be a long haul.

But wait, there's more from Wanganui, oh yes, loads more

In case you don't believe me that the River City has been a prolific creator of inventors, let me list, in a summary fashion, just a small sampling of the patents that have been lodged by Wanganui residents…

- In 1907, Charles Hope-Johnstone was given patent 23412 for 'an improvement for preparing milk for food'.

- In 1973, Robin Moore registered patent 169607, described as 'levelling means'.

- An 'automatic bowling or pitching machine' was registered in 1973 by Donald Brewer, patent 171202.

- Luckily for us Wayne Kirker (and others) registered in 1986 his patent number 218664, or else we may not have had a 'tub for washing'.

- I'm sure you've never invented a 'pelletising apparatus and process', but Fred Withers did, in 1988 and it was assigned patent 226865.

- Don and Ian Bullock registered 'improvements to sub-frames' in 1990 with patent 234042. Those sub-frames never were good enough.

- Leslie Broadmore did something clever enough to warrant giving an 'animal collar' patent 234987 in 1990.

- Anthony Walker was assigned patent number 238849 in 1991 for his 'drive-through gate' — always the best kind, I've found.

- Lucky for us that Mowtown Farm and Garden Limited registered in 1994 their patent 250638, 'improvements in/or relating to apparatus for collecting grass clippings from a lawnmower'.

- And most admirably, in 1994 Hazel Menehira (and others) registered their patent 265395, entitled most succinctly 'a chair'.

- And apart from these there's Dylan Whitford, who at 18 claimed to have created a way for cars to run on water. Hmm, I thought that was called a boat.

17. THE HUMAN BODY

Seeing eye glasses, valve replacements and breast protectors

A favourite area of invention is medical science. And this should be completely understandable – every inventor wants to create something that people will use, and what better thing to create than something they'll use on (or in) themselves.

Kiwi inventors other than those mentioned here have also seen this as a worthy goal. One inventor at age 88 came up with a way for 'poor people' (as he put it) to make their own bidet. In his estimation, not being a millionaire was no reason to have a dirty bottom. An innovative company in Auckland came up with a device for helping stretch the lower back, surely an apparatus that warrants a 15-minute, morning-slot TV advertisement if ever there was one. Tapanui flu could be said to be a New Zealand invention – this illness affecting people not just in the Southland region but all over the world. And it was Dr Harold Gillies, a doctor, surgeon and motorway off-ramp namesake, who pioneered the art of plastic surgery.

Kaspa

Friendly, if not a ghost

Now this is a cool idea. Two New Zealand inventors have come up with a way for blind people to hear what they can't see. Scientist Professor Leslie Kay, formerly from Britain but now living in Russell, Bay of Islands, teamed up with blind Auckland businessman Ivan Pivac to come up with a way to allow blind people to realise some of the freedom sighted people are afforded.

Professor Kay worked for the British government during the Cold War, developing underwater sonar technology for detecting submarines and other submerged objects. After his time with the British, Kay moved to New Zealand, working for many years as the Dean of the University of Canterbury's Engineering School, where he continued his work with sonar — this time, however, with a more humanitarian approach. Here Kay built on an invention of his from the mid-1960s: high-energy, octave-wide, frequency-modulated, very high-resolution ultrasonic sensing in air. If you know what all that means, then good luck to you. For the rest of us, it's enough to know that Kay's invention meant that he could start working on what seems to be a pet project for him, using sonar technology to detect objects for blind people.

In 1965 he invented the ultrasonic torch, which you point around you and it beeps if there's something in the way. In 1974 he modified this technology and made 'sonic glasses', a pair of spectacles with an ultrasonic sensor built in to warn you if there is anything in the vicinity.

In 1996 Kay approached Ivan Pivac with his idea of a fully functional system for using sonar to help blind people. The system was dubbed 'Kaspa', and basically it looks like a radio headset. It sends out sonar beams in a 3–4 m radius around the wearer, and then interprets the signals that 'bounce back'. The system can distinguish between different types of things that are returning signals, and converts the signals into different sounds that the user learns — for instance, glass gives a high-pitched shriek, people give a muffled sound and plants sound spongy.

The technology is so sophisticated that even butterflies can be 'seen', sounding like a soft fluttering. Indeed, Kaspa can identify about 300 different objects! Not only that, but the Kaspa system paints a three-dimensional soundscape, using 3D sound to approximate the place where the object is for the user.

The upshot of the whole idea is a $3500 device, consisting of a headset, headphones and a portable computer which in 1998 won the Saatchi and Saatchi Innovation in Communication Award, judged the best by a panel including Buzz Aldrin, Edward de Bono and William Gibson.

But perhaps the best advertisement for the system is Ivan Pivac — who granted has a vested interest, in that he markets Kaspa worldwide — but ironically it is Kaspa itself which allows him the freedom to travel the world, hearing his way through busy airports and hotels.

Cool Guard

The breast story in the book

In the 1960s, motor mechanic Max Rutherford was building his own car, from scratch, to compete in hill climbs and at the speedway. The 'MiniMax' went on to win the New Zealand hill climb championships, but by that time Max was overseas where he earned the title of chief mechanic for Jackie Stewart, the Formula One racing car driver. In 1969 Max successfully 'mechanicked' Jackie Stewart to victory on the Formula One circuit. Armed with an ability to make quick decisions, Max Rutherford returned home looking for a business opportunity....

In 1981 Ces Richie and Wynn Martin were coaching and administrating women's soccer. They saw a need for the breasts of women

Kaspa is also a fashion statement.

players to be protected from the harsh and rugged dangers of soccer. Everyone knows that a knock on the breast can be very painful for women, and there was no product that women could wear to provide the protection that nature neglected to provide. Ces and Wynn lived in the shadow of Mt Taranaki, whose soft, molten interior is protected by a hard shell-like exterior. No doubt drawing inspiration from the conical volcano, Ces and Wynn made a fibreglass mock-up of a chest protector which was held on by bra straps and could be worn under the soccer uniform. They gained a New Zealand patent, and a local company started production of the plastic protector.

Enter Max Rutherford again. And Robert Muldoon, whose policies for kick-starting the New Zealand manufacturing sector included tax breaks for companies exporting goods. In the early 1980s Max Rutherford got into the breast protection industry primarily for tax relief, and his company, Quality Performers, purchased the original company.

Quality Performers spent $27,000 on research in 1999 and developed a bra that is revolutionary worldwide. The Cool Guard has two plastic guards which are inserted into a specially designed sports bra. The bra is made from DuPont's Lycra and Tactel materials. The guards are unbreakable, Tupperware-style polypropylene and are moulded to spread impact. The plastic inserts can be removed to speed the cooling-down process.

There is a provisional US patent for Cool Guard, but Rutherford reckons that in some cases patents are more costly than the limited protection they provide are worth. None of the products has worldwide patents, and as a result the Hungarians, Mexicans, and Spanish have all had a go at copying the New Zealand breast protector with inferior and more costly products. Quality Performers' strategy is to keep the competition a few steps behind by continually innovating to ensure they lead the world.

And it is working. Throughout the 1980s and early '90s, Max Rutherford used to worry that Adidas, Nike or one of the other big sports manufacturers would copy his guard products and flood the market with cheap knock-offs. But in 1996, Adidas approached him to market the guards under the Adidas name. Currently the New Plymouth product is marketed internationally under the brand names of six different companies — all international leaders in martial arts, fencing and general sports goods. If you go into a sports good shop anywhere in the world and buy an Adidas, Kamikaze, Kwon, Blitz, Allstar (and

The bionic woman used Cool Guard.

shortly Budoland) breast protector you can be sure it was made in New Plymouth.

Currently, Rutherford ships about 15,000 breast protectors a year. Most of those end up in martial arts and fencing (Quality Performers has 80 percent of the world fencing market), but the new Cool Guard is perfect for general sports and promises to increase their market dramatically as it is suitable for the booming women's jogging, boxing and soccer markets.

A Singulairly (sic) good drug

Helping asthma sufferers

Asthma is a terrible affliction, which attacks by restricting its sufferers' ability to breathe. New Zealand has an appalling asthma record, with the disease killing around 130 New Zealanders, and costing the health system an estimated $375 million, per year. Asthma works by using chemical substances in the lungs called leukotrienes to attack the lungs, and cause inflammation, resulting in a distressing shortness of breath. The traditional way to treat asthma has been with a combination of steroids and other inhaler medications, treatments that are acceptable, but not remarkable. Then, in 1998 a team from the drug company Merck & Co announced a breakthrough new drug in asthma treatment called 'Singulair'. A key player in the team that created the drug was

Kiwi, Dr Jilly Evans.

Evans was born in Paparoa, North Auckland. She obtained a masters degree in cell biology at the University of Auckland, and completed a PhD at the University of British Columbia. She then completed some post-doctoral research in molecular biology at McGill University in Montreal, before joining the Canadian subsidiary of Merck and Co. in 1983. At Merck Frosst, she was part of the team that developed both Singulair, the anti-asthmatic compound, and Vioxx, a novel anti-arthritic drug. She moved to Merck in Pennsylvania in 1998 to become director of genomics and coordinate a Merck worldwide project to discover new drug targets from the human genome. (Genomics is the study of the effects of DNA and heredity, looking at the effects different genes, or DNA sequences, have on humans.)

With Singulair, the team came up with a chewable tablet, to be taken once a day, rather than the 'inhaler'-type asthma drugs we're all used to. This of course is a much preferable option for everyone, particularly children. The drug works by targeting and blocking the effects of the leukotrienes so the asthma effects are reduced. Singulair has been proven to improve the quality of life in asthma patients, and has helped wean many people off the inhaled steroids they used to use. It's been described as the biggest step in the treatment of asthma for over 20 years.

Dr Jilly Evans, helping people breathe more easily.

The Unifoot

Kiwi inventor foots it with the best of them

Kiwi David Dell woke up one night with a flash of inspiration — a user of walking sticks himself after suffering from back pains, he realised that there was a better way to make them. Conventional walking sticks have a single contact point with the ground, making them susceptible to slipping. David came up with the idea of replacing the normal rubber nosing at the bottom of the walking stick with a small plate made out of rubber. This would mean the walking stick had better contact with the ground, and it could also twist to conform to the contours of the terrain.

The result, the Unifoot, has been a great success. David created an initial prototype to prove the concept to himself, and then set out working with a plastics factory to create the product, which he patented in New Zealand and overseas.

The Unifoot is a startlingly simple idea, but a clever one that has a lot going for it. At $30 it's reasonably cheap, it can be fitted to the end of pretty much any walking stick or crutch, it allows the walking stick to stand up by itself, and it creates four points of contact with the ground, increasing the grip.

David was so proud of his invention that he decided to make a present of one to the Queen Mother, whom he had seen on the television using a 'common or garden' walking stick. He parcelled one up and sent it to the Queen Mum for her ninety-ninth birthday, and was pleasantly surprised to receive back this royal note of thanks and approval:

David Dell and his letter
from the Queen Mum.

Dear Mr Dell,

Queen Elizabeth the Queen Mother has just received the special walking stick which you so kindly sent Her Majesty at the time of her 99th birthday in August.

The Queen Mother is impressed by the ingenuity and simplicity of your new invention, and it is a birthday present which Her Majesty accepts with pleasure.

Signed
[Her lady in waiting]

Less than a year into the product's life the orders are flooding in. David has utilised the powerful and relatively cheap medium of the Internet to allow customers to order directly from him, cutting out the middle man and ensuring he has a presence worldwide.

The Unifoot has obviously solved a need that existed, and it's one of those special inventions you look at and think, 'Why didn't I think of that?'

The first aortic valve replacement

Medical innovation by a knight in sterile armour

Before 1958, if you contracted rheumatic fever or developed some other problem with a heart valve, the chances of you surviving were virtually nil. The valves in the heart are the muscles and sinews that control the flow of blood into and out of the heart, which in turn is in control of the circulation of blood around your body, so any major problem with these valves was fatal — and untreatable. That was until Kiwi surgeon Brian Barratt-Boyes (now Sir Brian) pioneered radical heart treatments at Greenlane Hospital in Auckland.

Brian Barratt-Boyes was born and educated in New Zealand, going overseas after gaining his MD to further his training in the United States. He returned to New Zealand in 1958 to head the heart unit at Greenlane Hospital, a role he was to fill for 30

years. In the late 1950s the practice of heart surgery was brand-new — Christiaan Barnard and others having pioneered techniques just a few years earlier — and Barratt-Boyes set about creating a world-class facility at Greenlane for the study of heart surgery.

Practising on sheep and cadavers, Barratt-Boyes and his team worked out a way to replace faulty heart valves in humans with those from donors, taking the heart valves from dead bodies soon after death and storing them, basically in a fridge, for up to four weeks. They reasoned, and it is still considered the case today, that using transplanted heart valves would be more successful, and more natural, than creating false valves out of synthetic materials. Barratt-Boyes still remembers the first time he performed the operation — he describes himself as 'pretty tense', but considered the operation went well. He still keeps in touch with his first guinea pig/patient, who was at the time only 16 years old. That she is alive and well today is testament to Barratt-Boyes' ground-breaking work.

Barratt-Boyes' work brought surgeons to Greenlane from all around the world, and turned the hospital into one of the foremost research institutes in the world. In turn, Barratt-Boyes travelled the world, then as he does now, learning and lecturing.

Another major breakthrough was Barratt-Boyes' work in 1968 on heart operations for infants. The problem with operations on

For the forward flow of blood to be maintained, heart valves have flaps that open and close in response to pressure changes in the ventricle. This allows blood to flow forward and prevents it from flowing backwards.

A — aortic valve

B — mitral valve

C — Regurgitation occurs when the valve flaps will not close properly.

D — Stenosis occurs when the valves develop scar tissue, this tissue can thicken and cause the flaps to lose flexibility.

E — If an aortic valve replacement from an organ donor successfully overcomes the initial immune system rejection it becomes a living part of the heart's tissue.

infants and small children is that the heart-lung machines used to replace the normal heart functions during the heart operation are too powerful for use on children. When you also take into account the small size of a baby's heart, it makes for a very tricky procedure. As a solution, Barratt-Boyes pioneered the use of 'profound hypothermia' on children.

It sounds a bit like science fiction, but basically the hypothermia technique involves cooling the infant's body temperature down from the normal 37 degrees Celsius, to about 15 degrees, at which point the blood stops circulating and the heart stops beating. Then surgery can begin, and the patient can stay in this state for up to 45 minutes.

Without a doubt, Barratt-Boyes' work at Greenlane during the late 1950s and '60s was among the finest medical work ever done by a New Zealander, and certainly — for a time at least — made New Zealand a world-class centre for medical research.

Plastic wheelchairs

Charity begins at home

At the back of the minds of most inventors is the pot-o-gold at the end of the rainbow. Success for Rob Buchanan, though, is not measured by the amount of money his inventions generate. Rob has set up a charitable trust called MEND, which endeavours to provide better living conditions for people all over the world, especially in developing countries in the Pacific and in Africa. The idea behind MEND is to improve life by innovations, and the inventor behind MEND is Rob himself.

In the early 1990s, as a yacht builder, Rob spent a lot of time sailing around the Pacific. He saw that disabled children in the Islands often had poor equipment to deal with their disabilities. Wheelchairs are not manufactured in the Islands, and imported models are very expensive. While an able-bodied man earns about NZ\$1 to \$5 per day in most developing

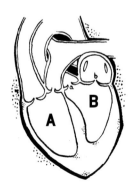

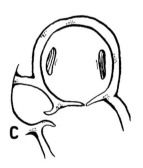

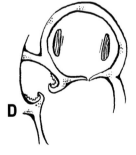

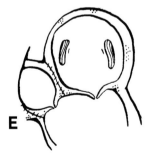

countries, the cost of a wheelchair is between NZ$100 and $500. Furthermore, wheelchairs that break down are very difficult to repair in remote settlements, as they are made from materials and technologies not available to the locals. The upshot is that vast numbers of people must remain at home or crawl on their hands and knees. Extreme poverty forces most people with disabilities to rely on charity for their mobility.

At first, Rob helped repair wheelchairs, then he thought about making new wheelchairs. Rob's idea was to make simple wheelchairs out of fibreglass and plastic. While back in New Zealand, Rob secured a grant from the Northland Development Board to allow him to design the wheelchair and make the mould.

The resulting MEND wheelchairs are cheap to make and buy, robust, and easy to repair — made of plastic, fibreglass and non-rusting metal, so it is non-rusting, low-cost, lightweight, colourful and easily transportable. It can also be manufactured locally, because the technology is simple.

The plan is to provide the moulds, the licence to manufacture and the expertise to set up manufacturing in developing countries. The licence fee allows MEND to continue to develop ideas, but while hundreds of the wheelchairs have been manufactured already, Rob has experienced difficulty in collecting the fee.

Rob Buchanan has also made a cheap

plastic or fibreglass toilet of which several hundred are in use in the Solomon Islands and around the Pacific. The toilet is hygienic, and can be flushed with a minimum (about an ice-cream container full) of precious water, or installed over a long-drop. Rob is also working on ideas to conserve fuel in countries where the land is being ravaged to provide wood for cooking fires, and many other humanitarian inventions.

If you feel that you want to help Rob Buchanan and MEND, you can e-mail him at **mend@voyager.co.nz.**

MEND wheelchair, made of fibreglass and plastic, late 20th century.

18. CLUTCHING AT STRAWS

The Buzzy Bee, hokey-pokey and the biggest drug company in the world

These things are the flotsam and jetsam of the book, the things we wanted to put in, but which were, on the whole, stretching the definition of 'Kiwi invention' a little. These are the things we remembered in our subconscious as having been told were Kiwi innovations, but for which we had no real proof. We set out to clarify the ownership of these things and, mostly, we have.

There were quite a number of other innovations and inventions that we were told by friends and others to investigate. It was suspected, for example, that it was a New Zealander who invented the cat's eye road marker; alas, this was not true. We were given an intriguing lead that the airport carousel was invented in New Zealand, a fact we struggled with but could not prove or disprove — despite the help of the convenor of the admirable website inventors.about.com. The trench periscope, the rotary lawnmower, Velcro and even the fax machine were interesting misconceptions that we investigated, only to find erroneous.

Here, then, are the remnants of our study, the inventions we wanted desperately to put in, even though at times we were, to be frank, clutching at straws.

Things with the word 'kiwi' in the title

We'll take what we can get

This section is a cold, hard, factual look at some things with the word 'kiwi' in them. Unfortunately trying to claim any of these things as Kiwi inventions is the very definition of clutching at straws....

First of all comes the kiwi bird. It is entirely indigenous to New Zealand. Nobody else can claim it, but while we should be proud of it, it is not an invention of ours at all.

Next comes the Kiwi boot polish. You're not going to like this. The company that made Kiwi polish started making it in 1906. It has become an international success story, expanding to Britain and the United States as well as France,

Canada, South Africa, Spain and Pakistan. The polish has made the word 'kiwi' a commonplace word all over the world. The company didn't invent shoe polish, just made a new kind, but that's not the bad bit. Here's the bit you won't like: the company is Australian. In 1901 William Ramsay visited New Zealand from Melbourne. He married a woman from Oamaru called Annie Meek. Later, back in Melbourne, he started making the soon-to-be-famous polish and his wife suggested the name 'Kiwi'. Kiwi polish is Aussie.

Ramsay's wife didn't suggest calling the polish 'Kiwi' after the people of New Zealand, because we weren't known as Kiwis until a little later. Indeed, the first time the kiwi is thought to have been used as an emblem was in 1887, when the University of Auckland used three kiwis on its seal. In 1905, the *New Zealand Herald* printed the first known cartoon where a kiwi was used to represent New Zealand, depicting a huge kiwi eating the Welsh rugby team. The existence of the Australian boot polish may in fact have added impetus to the naming of our people. During the First World War, the polish was widely used by Allied troops, and 'kiwi' became a well-known word. By the end of the war, it was common to call New Zealanders and things New Zealand, Kiwi. But that isn't a New Zealand invention either, it's just a name.

The kiwifruit was first grown in the Yangtze Valley in China. Its name in Chinese (which it would be fair to say is its real name) translates to mean 'Monkey Peach', maybe because while it is yummy like a peach, it is hairy like a monkey. In the 1940s and '50s, many New Zealand homes had a vine in their backyard. Because the tree was from China, and despite the fact that the fruit looks absolutely nothing like a gooseberry, the fruit was called the Chinese gooseberry by New Zealanders.

The fruit would have stayed named that if it hadn't been for the fact that during the late 1950s Turners and Growers began exporting the fruit to the United States. The Americans had a problem with the name 'Chinese gooseberry' as it seemed to describe another fruit altogether (and a yucky one at that). The Turner brothers put their thinking caps on and came up with 'melonettes'. Nice, yes, but anything to do with melons attracts a 35 percent import duty in America so the name was dropped. Figuring that the word 'kiwi' was the only word that foreigners would associate uniquely with New Zealand, they renamed the fruit 'kiwifruit'.

While New Zealanders did not invent the kiwifruit, we did perfect it by refining the plant to produce perfect fruit for human consumption. It remains today our largest horticultural export, and might be larger if it weren't for the fact that we also exported the plants so that other countries like Chile could benefit from the world kiwifruit boom. Some people see that as a mistake, but let's

Logically, Kiwi Shoe Polish is an Australian invention.

Chinese gooseberry, monkey peach, melonette or zespri – it looks like a kiwifruit to me.

look at it as a form of foreign aid.

Since we could not patent the kiwifruit, or even trademark the name, the kiwifruit marketing agency has come up with an appellation for New Zealand kiwifruit that no one else is allowed to use. Just like only sparkling wine from the French province of Champagne is allowed to be called 'Champagne', only kiwifruit from New Zealand can be called 'Zespri'. This way we'll all get rich!

The Buzzy Bee

Pull-along fun

In 1948 Hec and John Ramsey began production of a toy bee made of wood. It was pulled along by string and the rolling motion of its wheels made a clacking sound while the yellow wings spun. A fascinating and ground-breaking invention it might not be, but certainly a successful product both here and overseas. More than a great product, through fond association with our childhoods, the bee has become a Kiwi icon.

The bee has remained basically the same for all of its years of production. The plastic wings were, until the late 1960s, made of the same kind of fibre-board used to make old suitcases, and the clacker mechanism was updated in 1993 to suit modern safety standards, but apart from that it's the same

good old bee. It's interesting to point out that the wings were always made of plastic or fibre-board. They have never, ever, ever been made of wood. If you fondly reminisce about the old days with the image of a wooden-winged buzzy bee in it, then you are just plainly wrong.

There has always been only one real Buzzy Bee. The numerous patents and trademarks that protect Buzzy Bee have been bought and sold three times since the days of Hec Ramsey, along with the rights to several other of Ramsey's toys such as the 'Mary Lou' doll (from 1941) and the inventively named 'Richard Rabbit'. The tradition of Buzzy Bee remains strong.

Several million bees have been made, and sales are still very strong in New Zealand, but Buzzy Bee has never been a huge export. A big part of the Buzzy Bee business in the early 21st century is merchandising. The Buzzy Bee company, located in sunny Warkworth, has issued over 100 licences to other firms to manufacture and sell Buzzy Bee pyjamas, lunchboxes, stamps, schoolbags, jewellery, wrapping paper, paperweights, even women's underwear.

A New Zealand invention, a New Zealand success story? Maybe. Unfortunately, in the last year of last century a dark shadow of doubt was cast on the Kiwi origins of the Ramsey Buzzy Bee....

An old codger called Vernon Davenport spoke up in the media about having worked in

the Ramsey factory at the time of the bee's creation. Vernon (if that is his real name) says a guy called George Steel (a likely sounding name) brought a toy bee from America and showed it to Hec Ramsey. In another version of the story, the bee importer was Ramsey's own sister. Either way, the American 'bee', (which was even called 'Buzzy Bee') according to both stories 'was flat, about one and a half inches thick, timber, with the centre gouged out where the noise contraption went. It had coloured paper stuck to its body instead of paint... Hec looked at it and decided to make his own version. Within three months we were making batches of 5000 to 10,000.'

According to our patent experts, the rounded, painted bee that we know is a sufficient departure from the alleged American bee to warrant a new patent, and to be in fact a different toy. If the American bee had been any good, it surely would now be a worldwide success story, and not the historical cul-de-sac that it is. As New Zealanders certainly we must thank the Americans politely for their 'bee toy' but ask them, for both of our sakes, to stick to electricity and space travel and such and leave the important inventions to us. Similarly perhaps we should ask Mr Davenport (with love and respect) to leave the writing of the history of New Zealand inventions to the authors — unless he knows something about an American jetboat engine with coloured paper stuck to it.

If the Americans want our bee, we think we

speak for everyone when we say they'll have to come over here and take it off us. And anyone caught helping them (you know who you are, Vernon Davenport) will be tried for treason and hanged.

Glaxo

Today Bunnythorpe, tomorrow the world!

I think this story deserves to be in this book, even if it is clutching at straws in terms of being a genuine invention. Glaxo is the largest pharmaceuticals company in the world. When Glaxo joined Wellcome, the biggest cheque in the history of banking was written. When Glaxo joined SmithKline at the beginning of 2000, it created world headlines and once more established Glaxo as the largest pharmaceuticals company in the world. Glaxo started as a milk-drying business in Bunnythorpe, near Palmerston North, in 1920.

In 1856, Joseph Nathan left Australia where he had settled from England. He was trying to become a successful businessman and although Melbourne hadn't worked out for him, the small settlement of Wellington did. As Wellington grew, so did Nathan's business, and his family. At first he was a merchant, with an office to buy goods in London and a warehouse and distribution network to sell them in Wellington. His eight sons and four daughters were the key to the

Photograph of the great Joseph E Nathan, taken around 1900.

The slogan 'Builds Bonny Babies' was thought up by an employee who made Glaxo tins in Britain.

The tin room at Bunnythorpe.

blossoming of his business empire. He was a huge figure in the commercial life of early Wellington and the business soon grew and began to reach northward to the Manawatu and into the dairy industry.

In 1904, the idea of drying milk was new. Joseph Nathan assigned one of his younger sons to the job of setting up a factory to dry milk, making milk powder. A factory was built in Bunnythorpe to make this new product. After some hiccups, including a rival dairy owner burning down the first two Bunnythorpe factories, the Nathans registered a brand name for their new dried milk in 1907. They called it Glaxo.

Glaxo didn't take off straight away. With the slogan 'Builds Bonnie Babies' the product was marketed in England and in New Zealand as a milk food for infants. With the First World War came an incredible demand for the dried milk as supply for soldiers. The Glaxo arm of the company became bigger than its parent company, and with the addition of vitamin D to their milk products, Glaxo London and New Zealand began, in 1936, to move into the pharmaceutical research and production business.

Betnovate, Ventolin, Farex, Complan, Beconase, Becotide, Zovirax and Flixotide are among the many familiar products manufactured and marketed

by Glaxo. As the company grew, the worldwide headquarters shifted to London. As GlaxoWellcome, the company had 76 operating companies and more than 50 manufacturing sites worldwide — and seven products in the world top 50. With a turnover of $24 billion in 1998 and a workforce of some 59,000 worldwide, it spent about $6 billion a year on research and development. Today, GlaxoSmithKline New Zealand is a small part of GlaxoSmithKline worldwide which, through a series of buyouts and mergers, has become one of the largest companies in the world.

Kiwi food

Surely we made hokey-pokey?

If you're anything like us, you rank junk foods such as cheese-flavoured corn snacks with the computer and the motor car as some of the most important inventions of the modern world. What hollow existences we would lead without Twisties, without the Moro and Minties? How impoverished would our culture be if there were no foods like these to unite us?

One thing that is quickly apparent when you travel overseas is that different countries celebrate different sets of junk foods. Some are universal, such as Coca-Cola, but most are regional. But are the junk foods of New Zealand really native foods, or are they imported and named to suit us? It may indeed be clutching at straws (or at least clutching at potato-sticks) but this is a round-up of which of our cherished brands are really ours and which are foreign.

Let's start with some disappointments, and before I go on let me say that national pride must take a back seat to truth, at least in the following few paragraphs. Marmite and Vegemite are not New Zealand products at all. Marmite was invented in the UK and first imported to New Zealand by the Sanitarium company around the time of the First World War. Vegemite was invented by an Australian pharmacist in 1922 (he was mixing brewer's and baker's yeasts to try and make a better

yeast for brewing). If you still want to eat it, that's your decision.

Hokey-pokey ice cream is ours! Other countries have the confection that we call hokey-pokey. It is simply caramelised sugar, given little bubbles with the addition of soda. Honeycomb, humbug and butter-brickle are all hokey-pokey-like, but nowhere else is it put into ice cream. In America, Rocky Road ice cream has lumps of stiff toffee in it, but it's not the same stuff at all. Hokey-pokey ice cream was first sold during the Second World War by Meadowgold Ice Cream and nobody really knows where the name came from. The recipe has changed a little — originally, the hokey-pokey was made in big sheets and smashed up with hammers, so that the hokey-pokey lumps were rough, with hard edges. Now the hokey-pokey is made in roundish pellets, but it's all good. Altogether in New Zealand, somebody is eating about five million litres of hokey-pokey in a year. You know who you are.

Do you think of Weet-Bix as being

Get more go on Moro, all the energy you need to turn the page.

Hooked on chocolate.

brought to New Zealand in about 1965 and we began to make corn snacks.

Rashuns are the most New Zealand cheese-flavoured corn snack. Nowhere else in the world are Rashuns made. The recipe (the shape and the flavour) was invented here, and they are exported to some Pacific islands. The name comes from a combination of 'Rations' and 'Rashers' — for the bacon flavour. Twisties are the first New Zealand corn snacks (having been made now for 35 years) and the next most Kiwi. According to the manufacturer, the 'puffy worm shape' is probably not ours, and the flavour isn't either, and neither is the name (there are 'Twisties' in Australia but they are a different snack) but the combination is all ours, and like Rashuns they are exported to French Polynesia. Other snacks are not at all Kiwi, but are made under licence from overseas companies; this includes Cheezels, Burger Rings, Big-Uns, among others.

We've managed to come up with quite a few successful chocolate bars, but none that has taken the world by storm. The Moro is our best known bar by far. The recipe is New Zealand, probably based on the overseas Mars bar, and first made in 1968. The Crunchie doesn't belong to us; it's British. The Pinky was invented in New Zealand in the 1960s. Buzz Bars and the Perky Nana are also uniquely ours. The Buzz Bar goes back to the 1930s. Cadbury chocolate bars (Dairy Milk, Caramello, Energy etc) are available all over the world. Every country occasionally brings

essentially New Zealand? Well, once again it is Australian. Even the song 'Kiwi kids are Weet-Bix kids' was originally 'Aussie kids are Weet-Bix kids'. When I first heard that jingle on television in Australia, I almost choked. Looking back I was naive to be fooled. If you look closely, the kids in the ads are obviously Australian. Again, if you still want to eat Weet-Bix, go ahead. It's up to you.

With cheese-flavoured corn snacks, there is good news and bad news. The technology for making the snacks was developed overseas. The machines that make them were developed from the machines that spun the foam for inside car seats. This technology was out a new flavour which will last a while then disappear. New Zealand has spawned one flavour of chocolate which has persisted, and now is an international favourite. In the early 1990s the Dunedin chocolate researchers came up with putting cherries and bits of biscuit into chocolate bars and New Zealand gave the world Black Forest!

Minties and Jaffas and Snifters belong to Australia. Fruit Bursts (those chewy things wrapped like Minties) were invented here (not too long ago) and have gone on to conquer Australia.

New Zealand has one brand of soft drink of our very own which has survived. Lemon & Paeroa is now owned by the Coca-Cola company, but is marketed only in New Zealand. It all began in 1904 when Dr Arthur Wollman tasted some mineral water bubbling from a spring in a cow paddock in the Hauraki Plains area. He thought it was good and he should have known, for he was the government balneologist. In those days the government had, on their payroll, balneologists — scientists whose field was the medical benefits of mineral waters. This was a very important matter for early New Zealand because our major tourist attraction in the 19th and early 20th centuries was our mineral waters. People came from all over the world to bathe in the warm springs and drink our spring water.

In 1907 a company called Menzies and Co. bought the access to the water and began to bottle it. They mixed it with lemon and called it Paeroa & Lemon. Their major market was in the city of Auckland, and it began to get expensive to transport the water there, so they copied Wollman's chemical analysis of the water exactly and thus made a synthesised version. They reversed the name to 'Lemon & Paeroa', and it has continued to sell until today. Paeroa's neighbouring town, Te Aroha (which, if you have never been there, is beautiful!) also at one stage had a soft drink named after it. 'Lemon & Te Aroha' (if that is what it was called) has not survived, and the people of Paeroa have been unbearable ever since, erecting a huge brown L&P bottle on their main street.

But the best stories in the world of confectionery may be lost to us forever. The process of enrobing shaped marshmallow in chocolate may be a New Zealand invention. If it isn't, many of the resulting candies certainly are. The records of Cadbury and Hudsons cannot confirm it, but it is thought that the chocolate fish is a uniquely New Zealand confection. The marshmallow and chocolate Easter egg too may be uniquely our invention. Both appeared around 1955 as novelties at Cadburys.

The most interesting thing that comes out of all this is that companies who manufacture these foods have people researching and 'designing' foods, snacks, bars and lollies. If the lollies sell, they stay, but either way they remain just 'recipes' to the companies that make them. For this reason the history of some of our Kiwi icons has been lost to us.

L&P — would it have been world famous in New Zealand if they'd called it P&L?

19. PATENTS AND THE BATH-B-SMALLER

Patents, patience and legal issues

The authors of this book came up with a brilliant idea for a new Kiwi invention — a bath divider for making the bath smaller when bathing infants. In this chapter we take our Bath-b-Smaller through the initial stages of securing a patent to protect the (obviously brilliant) idea from being copied and cashed in on by others. We are not concerned here with making sure an invention is a good idea, or that it works, or making sure that people want to buy it. We are focusing on the process of ensuring the idea is novel and ours alone and then protecting the idea, by patent, from being copied.

The patent process

A long, winding and pricey road

The process of protecting your invention is lengthy and complex. There are three forms of protection for inventors: design copyright, trademarks and patents. These three protections are cousins, similar conceptually but differing in implementation. The crucial step for most inventors is securing a patent.

A patent gives you exclusive use of your invention for 20 years. After that, your idea belongs to society and anyone is free to copy it. Worse, when you first apply for your patent you have to give a complete description of how it works. The patent information is public, so when your patent expires, everyone knows your 'secrets'. For this reason, some companies (like Coca-Cola) rely for protection from copycats on being the best or the best known, or on keeping the manufacturing method a close secret.

Getting a New Zealand patent protects you only from infringements in the New Zealand marketplace. To get wider-ranging patents you simply (but expensively) have to repeat the New Zealand patent process for each territory in which you want the monopoly on your invention.

Step One: having the idea

Like many true inventors, our invention was born out of necessity. Sort of. One night, whilst bathing his son, David realised that the lad was only taking up a small fraction of the volume of the bath, but that he was forced to fill the entire thing with water. In Auckland, where David lives, he has to pay for every drop that comes out of the tap, whether it's gainfully employed in getting peanut butter out of his son's hair or not. So, in a brainstorming session, we came up with the idea of what we then called the 'Bath Divider'. It is designed to reduce the volume of the bath when bathing small objects like sons.

Step Two: describing the invention
We approached Tim Jackson of Baldwin Shelston Waters (a law firm specialising in patents), who agreed to patent our genius invention for us. Before Tim could start, we had to describe exactly what it was we wanted to patent. (See the box on describing the Bath-b-Smaller.)

In addition to describing the invention, we needed to settle on a name in order to market it. Tim Jackson advised that choosing a name needed care. Some of his tips for the naming process are given over the page.

Step Three: patent search
An invention can only be patented if nobody else has patented it before you. To find out if there are any existing patents on inventions like yours, you have to carry out a patent search. You can do some of the research on the Internet (check out the Intellectual Property Office at www.iponz.govt.nz); you

can go to the actual patent office in Wellington and look through their files; you can hire a company to do a quick search for around $100; or you can hire a lawyer to do it for you — this is substantially more costly at about $800, but also much more comprehensive. You don't have to do the patent search, but if

Describing the Bath-b-Smaller

To: tim.jackson@bswip.co.nz
From: 'David and Jon'
Re: Bath Divider

We are not fully sure about the actual details of the bath divider. Let me try to firm it up now. The child is bathed in the side of the bath not occupied by the bath divider. The divider just takes up room in the bath, so as to save water. It is an inflatable bag with a flat, sand-filled bottom.

The bag is the width of a bath, and as long as half the bath. It is designed so that the bag fits neatly into and fills one end of the bath. The bag is as high as a bath, too. The bottom is rectangular in shape, so are the sides and ends. It fits into the square end of the bath. Water will go around it to some extent but this does not matter, because it still saves as much water as its volume (when the bath is full). One further detail is that instead of just being one solid bag, there are several sections. One main section, and three extra sections. Inflating just one, or all of these, can change the size of the bath divider, allowing for different-sized children. It is made of the same stuff as a good-quality beach ball, and can be entertainingly coloured.

The main difficulty is fixing the divider to the bottom of the bath. Hopefully a good quantity of sand will do the trick. We too thought of a division that completely sealed one section of the bath off, but we can think of no watertight method to fix this to the bottom and sides of the bath. It would have to be completely watertight, and removable. I'm not sure we have the technology!

Naming your invention: some tips

Avoid being too descriptive of your product. Competitors may legitimately use the same words when advertising their product. So, for example, they could say, 'Try our bath divider because ...'. This rules out calling our invention the Bath Divider.

Making up a word (such as Kodak or Zespri) is best because it doesn't mean anything in itself but, through use, can become distinctive of your product. Combination words are good too (e.g. Janola – a combination of Jan and Nola, the inventors' wives names).

If you intend to export your product be careful of translation problems with major languages (e.g. the made-up word Pajero in colloquial Spanish apparently means 'wanker'). You may suddenly find that no one in certain countries wants to buy your product.

Taking the above into account, the Bath-b-Smaller was the name we decided on – still a bit descriptive perhaps, but we liked the sound of it. It has a certain ring. Not a ring around the bath, you understand, but around the term.

you don't you could spend heaps of time and money developing the product and filing the patent application only to find out that someone has already patented your idea.

The patent search took two weeks, and Baldwin Shelston Waters supplied us with the search results — a report on all the items that were in any way similar to ours. Amazingly, there were other patents a bit like Bath-b-Smaller, but luckily there were no New Zealand patents which we would be infringing, so we were all clear to start the patent application.

Step Four: patent application
Provisional patent

One of the big traps in the patenting process is that you must not publicise details of your invention before you apply for a patent, or you will lose the right to patent it — forever. This can be a pain in the posterior because a certain amount of publicising (such as visiting trade shows with your prototypes) may be crucially helpful in your development and you may want to do these things before you spend money applying for a patent. Another reason for securing a provisional patent is that a full patent application must include complete specifications of the invention. These are quite complicated documents to produce and may take a lot of time. The provisional patent provides you with a year's protection, during which time you are free to publicise and develop, and even manufacture

and market the invention safely. A provisional patent will cost you $80 for government filing fees and about $1500 for a lawyer to write the application — although you could attempt it yourself. Whenever you see 'Pat Pending' on a product, that means it is protected by a provisional patent.

We were so excited about our Bath-b-Smaller that we skipped the provisional patent and went straight for the full patent.

Full patent

Within a year of applying for the provisional patent, you must apply for a complete patent. The process here is a little more arduous than before; the onus is on you to prove that your invention is novel and unlike anything else. To do this, you provide a 'complete specification' and drawings. The complete specification is a quite complex legal document. For the Bath-b-Smaller, it ran to nine pages including the drawing. (An excerpt is shown in the box.)

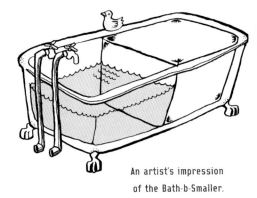

An artist's impression of the Bath-b-Smaller.

The patent office fee for a full patent is just $250, but it can cost thousands to have patent attorneys write the specifications for you.

Once you've lodged your application with the patent office, the patent examiner may debate your application, or ask for more information. If they accept that your invention deserves a patent, they advertise that they are probably going to issue you a patent. Anyone can then lodge an objection to your patent application if they feel they have grounds — and even if they don't, sometimes. It's been known for large companies to protest the patent applications of their smaller competitors simply to slow them down or put them out of business. Again, remember this whole process is a commercial one, so if you can't afford to fight in court, you may not come out on top, no matter how morally correct you believe yourself to be.

Step Five: Reaping the rewards

Finally, you are issued with a full patent. So there it is — a long process (18 months to two years on average) and a costly one (if you complete the process for $4000 you'd be doing well), and this is just for the legal side of things. This is on top of the hundreds of hours and thousands of your own dollars you've probably already pumped into your invention. Makes you wonder why anyone would bother ...ah, but it might be another 'Ghost'...(see Chapter 11).

And after all that, how much protection have we got for our world-beating bath thingy? In some ways it doesn't afford much protection at all — indeed, our lawyer describes a patent as a 'licence to sue'. Patents are covered under commercial not criminal law. The police won't help you stop copycats; you'll need to take them to court for what could be a very expensive battle.

However, with your full patent in hand you may now sell your patent rights, lease them to someone, license out manufacture, manufacture the product yourself — pretty much whatever you like. By the time this book reaches you, the Bath-b-Smaller patent (NZ Pat. # 504593) should be ours. Don't hesitate to call us if you would like a licence to manufacture!

INDEX